For my parents,
Audrie and 'Comrade'

and once again
with love to Felicity

First published in 2018 by
PRIMAVERA BOOKS LIMITED

Text copyright © 2018 Alasdair Scott Sutherland.
Layout and design copyright © 2018 Primavera Books Ltd

British Library Cataloguing-in-Publication Data.
A CIP record for this title is available from the British Library

ISBN 978-0-9557892-2-9

Cover design by Willie Landels
Design and typesetting by Jim Harrison
Production by B&G Porteous
Printed and bound in Great Britain by CPi Antony Rowe.
Papers used by Primavera Books are natural, recyclable products
made from wood grown in sustainable forests.

The manufacturing processes conform to the
environmental regulations of the country of origin.

1 3 5 7 9 10 8 6 4 2

Primavera Books Ltd
www.primaverabooks.co.uk

AUTHOR'S NOTE

Audrie and Robin are themselves,
as much as I remember them.

Nearly everything and everyone in part
two of this story, first appeared in the bundle
of faded letters.

My father and my grandparents are
to an extent themselves, as I have imagined
them to be in the 1930s and 40s.

The Manns, the Berrys, the Garlands
and the Larsens are not Manns, Berrys,
Garlands or Larsens, but an approximation
of similar characters.

'Modern girls don't cry,
even if they feel like it.'

Dorothy Brunton, 1926

PART

ONE

Aberdeen, Scotland 1990s

Simultaneous arrival and departure announcements from different station platforms, made harder to understand by the accents, swirled into a cacophony of human and electronic interference. Doors were slammed, bags hoisted onto racks, a whistle sounded, there was a jolting and the train finally started to move.

I had taken a seat at the left side of the carriage, facing forward, and pressed my forehead against the window. A favourite part of my schoolboy visits to my grandparents had been arriving and leaving the city by train, and now I watched its slow process as the granite town centre opened up to Riverside Drive, revealing the dark waters of the Dee.

Coming back south, my spirits were always lifted as the sea came into view, but bustling tugs and launches, darting in and out between the giant oilfield service ships, had almost completely replaced the fishing fleets of my childhood. As the old train turned south along the coast, approaching Cove Bay, nothing but the beach with its rusted, overgrown wartime defence bunkers and gun emplacements lay between the railway line and the great grey spread of the North Sea.

I loved train journeys, that feeling of release coming at the start of every journey. To have a choice of how far to go, how quickly or how slowly, whether to disembark at the first or the last stop, to be able to change direction or even cancel and turn right round, and start again later, was for me the real freedom of travel.

In the reflection of the window, as the light faded, I recalled my earliest bus rides, at the age of four, when for the first time, my mother had allowed me to catch the green and yellow Southdown to school on my own. She walked me from our Sussex cottage, three hundred yards up to the main road. At Monkey Puzzle Corner, I was usually the only one waiting at the request stop. When I climbed into the open platform, the conductor had lifted me onto the seat right next to the luggage cubby hole, before running upstairs to ticket other passengers. A few minutes later, as the double-decker trundled past the huge army camp and into Maresfield, he clattered back down and stood over me. My head had come just to the bottom of the conductor's waistcoat.

'Where to?' As if he didn't know. I looked up, pointed to the badge on my blue blazer and held out a threepenny bit.

'St Nicholas? Right you are.' The conductor took the coin, clicked a few wheels on the ticket machine hanging from his chest, wound the handle, and presented me with the resulting white slip, which I slid carefully into my blazer breast pocket.

'Look after this and don't show it to *anyone*,' he whispered.

I looked up with concern. 'What about the inspector?' The conductor nodded gravely. 'Except the inspector.'

What mother today would allow a child of four to catch a bus on his own? I knew it wasn't that Audrie didn't care or couldn't be bothered. Probably she'd just wanted her two boys to be self-sufficient and independent as soon as they could.

My mother was an open-faced, attractive woman, not obviously beautiful, but with a joyous, unrestrained laugh, an enticing smile, an excellent figure and very good legs, of which she was always proud. Probably because of her own colonial childhood, sent back to England for school from the age of eight to eighteen, she wasn't given to demonstrating much emotion.

Perhaps determined to be both warm mother and stern father to us both after Robert's death, she succeeded in hiding her undoubted affection for her children, for while she gave us a happy childhood, she never resorted to actual expressions of love. This had its compensations. I was proud to be the one small schoolboy who never had to suffer the embarrassment of a weeping mother on the railway platform at the beginning of term.

It had first occurred to me in my twenties that I knew very little about Audrie's previous life. She'd always held her cards very close.

Other people's mothers were always happy to chat about their lives; but sitting with Audrie at home, in a car or a café, it was difficult to take a conversation further than a discussion of the garden, of today's news or some cousin's forthcoming wedding, and impossible to get her to talk about Ceylon. Even much later, when we were together again, eating dinner or quietly reading the papers on a Sunday visit, her responses to my questions – about her friends, or an item about Sri Lanka in the paper, or what she'd been doing – were constantly evasive. 'Oh, the usual, you know.' But of course I didn't know. For many years I wasn't that bothered, but like any child, I'd become more interested in my parents' earlier lives as I grew older and began to compare the fortunes fate had thrown us both.

As the train rattled on southwards, I opened the large bundle Audrie had given me earlier that afternoon. Letters and papers, bound together with ancient elastic ties and crimson ribbon, were wrapped in a gigantic dark red silk scarf, mottled and worn, which smelled of a combination of tobacco smoke, camphor and scent. There must have been hundreds, mostly blue air-letters or on thin sheets, folded neatly back into their envelopes. I didn't recognise the hand. Some were addressed to Audrie Finch Noyes in Colombo, or later in Sussex, but many had originally been posted to Mrs Robert Sutherland in Cape Town, South Africa. I had no idea what she could have been doing there.

'Ma, what would you like me to do about these?' I'd been looking for a pill she'd dropped behind her chair, when I put a hand on the bundle and pulled it out.

She looked up from her book. 'Ah, I've been thinking about them since I decided to move on,' she'd said. 'The Manorfield flat is very small. I was going to burn them all, but when you kept asking about Com, I thought…' She looked away out of the window for a few seconds and then, straight at me, as though she'd only now made a decision. Her blue eyes glittered in her tired, lined face.

'Are they my father's? Tell me about him.' I knew that although my father's name was Robert, Audrie and all his friends had always called him Comrade, or Com, a legacy of a joke from school.

'Some are. I think you'd better have them, now.' She ignored my other question. 'There's nothing much, letters and papers I kept from Ceylon, all very old. I gave you the Kandy cigarette box, didn't I? These are all I have left now.' She paused and glanced at her wedding photograph on the side table. 'Well, when you look at them, you'll know as much about him as I could ever tell you.'

The engraved silver box was the only thing I owned that had belonged to Com. It had lain on our bedside table in London for many years, and almost every time I opened it, I'd wondered what kind of man he'd been. I turned the pile over and tidied up a loose string.

'I used to ask Robin about him, but he was only seven when we came home, wasn't he?' She'd batted away my question with a gesture. 'Perhaps put them away when you get home,' she suggested. 'And then, one day, later on. You know.' Recognising her reluctance to go on, I kissed her cheek. 'OK, later on, if you say so. I'll put them in the strongbox.'

Now, in the train, as I riffled through the pile, looking at postmarks, dates and the senders' names, only a few letters appeared to be from my mother. Seeing her familiar hand on an envelope had always cheered me, given me an optimistic lift, as much as did coming home from school for the holidays, or later, working abroad, flying back from Hong Kong and coming to see her. Her letters were such a contrast to her conversation. Although only personal about her own life when it came to dates and plans, they were always practical, carefully considered and full of good sense.

'It's not unusual, my mother was much the same,' Felicity had once confided over dinner. 'Perhaps it's their generation. And like her, Audrie's a strong, independent woman, clever and perceptive. But she keeps so much in, she never shows her cards.'

Felicity had the enviable ability to sum people up after half an hour's acquaintance. Very early on in our relationship, she had pointed out that while Audrie was more self-sufficient and capable than most women of her age, she was remarkably un-motherly, made no fuss of me or anyone. Since Audrie was my mother, I hadn't noticed.

I'd assumed all women maintained a private, inner self, depended on no one, and knew how to change fuses, fix punctures and deal with banks.

'I'm sure it's rubbed off onto you,' Felicity had maintained. 'I've never known you ask for help doing anything, even making the bed.'

I started as the whistle sounded. It was hard to resist having a further look in the bundle. I pulled out a thin brown envelope, clearly postmarked Bletchley, Bucks, 22 September 1953, with a twopenny stamp bearing King George's head, and addressed to Mrs A.J. Sutherland. I slid out the card. In pencil, I had written,

Dear Mum, I have arrived safely. Thank you for the card.
Robin sent me one too! Are you well? Love SUTHERLAND.

God Almighty. She had kept everything. I would have been, then, what, seven, nearly eight, starting my first term at prep school and after just one day, already using my surname like all the other little boys.

With Robin always away at school, I'd grown up for the most part as an only child, playing on my own or wandering alone through the woods behind the cottage. I was always startled when people talked about how they had hated being sent off to school and torn away from their parents.

'Boarding school is parents' self-inflicted wound,' people say today. 'It teaches your children that they don't need you.' But for me, a school with dozens of other small boys to play with, deep woods and undergrowth in which to build camps, and plenty of trees to climb, was heaven, compared with the silence of a country cottage in the heart of Sussex heathland.

I put the cards and letters back into the pile. Outside it grew darker. The train slowed down into Stonehaven, crossed over the main road, clattered across a set of points outside the station, and once through the town, set a new course inland. I found myself gazing out of the window for a while, and then, giving in to curiosity, shuffled through the letters again. A grey business envelope, bigger than most of the old blue letters, stuck out among the pile on my knees. It was addressed to Miss Audrie Finch Noyes at Glenugie Estate, Maskeliya, Ceylon. I stared at it for a few seconds, unsure of the right thing to do, but then decided.

The letter inside was on headed paper from *Cutler, Palmer & Co., Wines & Spirits, Steuart Place, Colombo*, and dated July 1937. The handwriting was neat, obviously well practised, of a consistent size without high loops or swirls. It may have been written on business letterhead, but it was clearly a love letter:

> *Dearest Audrie*
>
> *I'm getting quite angry at all this useless waste of time and you have no idea what a desperately weary place Colombo is when you're not here. The office is boring. Bridge makes me sick. The Garden Club gives me a pain in the neck. In fact, being back in Colombo again after one marvellous weekend with you is like a condemned prisoner who's escaped for a couple of days and then is recaptured and shoved back in his cell again. Kay and I got well beaten in the bridge tournament last night. I was holding the most awful cards but small wonder considering how lucky in love I am.*
>
> *I've just put down the receiver darling and I must say I'm feeling much brighter and happier for our talk. I'm so glad you'll meet me at Hatton on Friday. It will give me one extra precious hour with you and that means so much to me. Take care of yourself, and don't put too much water in your bath in case you drown because I'd have to drown myself too.*

So that was what she'd kept in that bundle all this time. Com's letters – but so many, from where to where? This one was obviously very soon after they met. I glanced at the date again. July 1937. I slid the letter back into the envelope, folded them all back into the silk and stuffed it into my bag.

So what does that tell me, I wondered. My father worked for a Wines and Spirits company, they met, he wrote her witty love letters with more than a touch of PG Wodehouse, and he played bridge. And why has she never talked about him? Some day, a date I didn't want to think about, I'd find the time to go through it all. I pulled out a file of monthly client reports. Another hour to Edinburgh, and then the flight home.

'Not now. One day, later on,' she had said. 'You know.'

'Ah, there you are. How was she this time?' Felicity called as I came in. 'Any stronger?'

'Much the same,' I said. 'She's gearing herself up to move to the retirement home. There's a small serviced flat they've offered her, with care staff. She can look after herself or if she wants, there's a restaurant. But she hasn't decided when. I'll go back in a few weeks' time. Meanwhile…'

I leaned over, lifted her hair and nuzzled the back of her neck.

'Do it properly.' She turned in the chair, stood up, put her arms around me and kissed me. We stood locked together for a while, until she leaned back.

'Nothing more about your Pa?'

'Very little. No great progress. Didn't want to speak about him, or Ceylon.' We unfolded ourselves and sat down. 'But she did give me an old scarf full of her memorabilia. It's huge. Tell me about your day.'

'Quite good. Successful meeting and lunch with Harpers. Sandy will use the new range for her January cover.' Felicity worked for a fashion house, and her work was a constant dazzle of launches and shows.

'Well done, how did you convince her? Not the fatal charm again?'

''Fraid so. Plus two glasses of champagne. Will you try again next time you go up?'

I picked up the pile of post on the desk and began to glance through it. 'I will try again, in a while, but gently,' I said. 'She backs off if I ask the same questions every time.'

Tall, and with a large straight nose, red-brown hair and pale skin, in those days I looked more Irish than Scots. I affected expensive-looking suits from an inexpensive tailor in Fulham, and my waist size hadn't increased much over the years, in spite of the fact that the most exercise I took regularly was the long walk from arrival gate to immigration control at various airports. I'd been healthy and reasonable-looking in my twenties and thirties, but in my fifties, my face already carried the evidence of too many late nights and early mornings, too many pre-dawn flights and midnight returns, during my time working around Europe and the Far East.

Felicity knew that as I grew older, I'd become increasingly curious about my parents' lives. So far, in the absence of any hard facts, I'd pieced together the story as best I could, but Audrie was well over eighty, and we knew there wasn't much time left.

Years before, Felicity had asked Audrie about her life with my father, but had met with a brick wall. Audrie changed the subject, asking Felicity instead about her work or her own family. Even when Felicity discovered that her own favourite aunt had been a bridge-playing friend of Audrie's, Betsy had admitted that she, too, had tried. 'I told her about my war, Bletchley Park and so on, and asked her about Ceylon a couple of times, but she never dropped a stitch,' Betsy had confided.

'It was such a tragedy,' Audrie's cleaner had said, when as a ten-year-old I asked if she knew about my father. Mrs Page had been housekeeper to Audrie's parents before the war, and usually chatted non-stop as she worked. But she would never be drawn further, and must have been instructed that the subject was strictly off-limits.

'Let's have a glass.' Felicity led us into the kitchen and reached into the fridge for a bottle of Sauvignon. 'Darling, you mustn't let it worry you. It's quite normal among her generation. She'll tell you one day.'

'That's the point, maybe there is some huge story she doesn't want to talk about. I know some old men won't talk about what they did in the war, but it's not as though Audrie was some sort of resistance heroine, is it? After all, I don't think I need protecting from the truth.'

I picked up an airmail letter. 'Oh, yes, sorry,' said Felicity. 'That came today. USA postmark. I took a sneak. San Francisco.'

'It's Robin.' I slit the envelope open and started reading. 'He's thinking of coming home; he'll sell the business and retire back here. He's going to stay with Mum. That's good; he can help look after her.'

When we next spoke, Audrie said she was thrilled that Robin would soon be coming home. 'By the way,' she revealed, 'I fell over in the garden.' Nothing serious, she stressed, but enough to make her sure it was time to move into that flat at Manorfield.

Normal people 'fall over', I thought. Old people 'have a fall'. Obviously Audrie didn't see herself as that old.

'Darling,' she went on,' I drove over to see them and there's a vacancy now. I gather Joyce Blackwood already lives there, she says it's not too bad, and there are several good bridge players.'

Naturally, I encouraged her. Once installed, Audrie would have friendly neighbours a few steps away, access to the gardens, help in the flat, and nursing staff at hand if necessary. I offered to come and help her move, but independent as always, she said no need for me to worry, the Manorfield people would take care of it. She'd take only enough furniture for her bedroom and sitting room.

'I'll leave the rest here at Bramblings,' she insisted, 'in case you want to come up to see me and stay the night. Then, once I'm settled we could put it on the market.'

By the following month, it was all done, and when I went to see her in the new flat, Audrie was comfortable, and sure it had been the right thing to do. But there was still that short, dry cough.

———————

'Darling, I've been thinking about you and those letters of your father's,' Felicity announced one evening as we set out to walk to our local restaurant. 'I'd love to see Sri Lanka. If you really do want to know what their life was like, why don't we go?'

'Go back? You're right. Good idea,' I said. 'It might help get Audrie to talk about those days.' I was thinking about the photographs in the old albums she had given me – their bungalow, their clubs, the beaches, the hotels.

'But it's not just about you finding out about your father,' Felicity insisted. 'We do need a real break. You even more than I do.' Aside from the odd weekend, the pressure of work, especially hers, had meant we hadn't taken a proper holiday for years.

'Agreed. Not just a pilgrimage for me,' I assured her. 'We can lie by a pool for a week and read.' We crossed over the Fulham Road by the hospital. An ambulance shrieked up and turned into the emergency bay.

'Doing nothing for a week, sitting in the sun, no appointments,' she smiled. 'And then perhaps a tour. But would Audrie tell us where to go, what to see?'

'We can try,' I offered. 'Let's call her and ask. It's not exactly her favourite subject.'

Upon our arrival at Il Frantoio, Bucci insisted on kissing us both, and showed us to a table in the far corner. For the next two hours we forgot completely about family problems. As we walked home later, I realised that Felicity had talked me into something I now very much wanted to do. I loved her, she was as usual completely understanding, and we had been so happy together for so long. After twenty years, it was time to ask once more.

'Darling, I know you did say yes, but what about getting married before we go? I could easily book at Chelsea.'

'You darling. I know I did.' She took my arm and snuggled against my shoulder. 'But no, it's nonsense. I'm not going back there. Been there, done that, got the ring.' Both of our first weddings had been at the Chelsea Register Office, and Felicity had always made fun of the idea of going back.

'Imagine,' she said as I unlocked the front door, 'standing outside the Town Hall again with some stupid hat over one eye, and all our friends laughing. I love you very much but I'm not going back there.'

When Robin finally returned to the UK, he called to arrange for us to get together in London. We would meet for lunch at a restaurant we'd often used in the seventies, before I left for Hong Kong and Robin moved to America.

Waiting at the barrier for the Gatwick train, I wondered how my brother, normally reserved, would greet me after so long, and was surprised to receive a big hug, with our teenage cry, '*Fratello mio!*' There was a trace of American in his speech, and Robin was much bigger than I remembered, his complexion florid, and his curly hair completely white.

We walked out into Buckingham Palace Road, exchanging family news. Robin's two sons were well, living with their mother in the West Country. But his brief answers seemed guarded and I couldn't help wondering what had prompted his return. What had happened to Robin's American wife, or to his San Francisco business? I would wait for the right moment to ask.

At the restaurant door, Mimmo was at first bemused, then effusive. 'Eh! Signor Sutherland, Robin! And Signor Sutherland, Alasdair!' he cried. 'I saw the booking but didn't know who to expect. Both of you, after so long!' The old proprietor saw us to a table at the back, chatted to us and having taken the order, left us to it.

Robin's attitude changed. 'I'll get straight to the point,' he confided as soon as we were alone. 'It's rather a bore. I've got a cancer.' It was serious, a colon tumour, he explained, but they had found it early. 'I'm due for an operation as soon as they can schedule it, probably at the end of the month.'

I was horrified. 'Colon? How beastly, I'm so sorry to hear it, you poor old thing. But that's very curable now, isn't it? Where will you stay afterwards? Who will look after you?'

'It'll be fine. According to the doc,' Robin continued, 'I'll need one of those horrible colostomy bags, but only for six months. Then, you go back and they connect your gut up again, and the hard part's over, back to normal. When they send you home, post-op, they arrange for carers to come in every day.'

This news was a shock, but I was also surprised to be told. Robin had always been happy to share his successes, but very rarely his problems. Even in his thirties, Robin had still treated me as the much younger brother that I was. Perhaps the years without seeing each other had finally changed his attitude.

'That sounds good. But where will you go? When you come out? Will there be follow-up treatment?'

'It'll probably be Craigforest.' One of Audrie's local hospitals. 'They said it will depend on the operation. If they're sure they've got it all out, it may be OK.'

'Let's hope so. Let's drink to that.' We raised our glasses and drank. 'What about Ma, does she know?'

Robin hadn't yet told Audrie, or his two sons, but would call them later. All being well, he hoped to stay at Audrie's house while he was recovering.

'I'll go home there if I can,' he continued. 'I gave my address as Bramblings, so Craigforest is the nearest. It means I'm definitely back for good. How's Felicity?'

It made complete sense for Robin to have come back to the UK, so as to be looked after by the NHS instead of some horrendously expensive American hospital. But now, he obviously needed to talk about something else.

'She's fine, wonderful, we're very happy.' As the linguine arrived, I changed the subject.

'I've been trying to get Ma to tell me about their life in Ceylon. You were seven when Pa died; do you remember anything about him?'

'Not much, sorry.' He shook his head. 'He sang a lot when he was at home. But it wasn't often. Did I tell you about Marina? She chucked me out.'

So that was it, not just the cancer. Robin had decided to come home after breaking up with his second wife, which meant that until he sold the business, he was without funds, work or a home. For Audrie to have him nearby at her house would be a blessing. Once Robin recovered, he'd be back at home, able to visit her at Manorfield and make her move there much less of an upheaval. On the other hand, the last thing she needed to worry about was her older son needing nursing care at home after the cancer operation.

I offered to come up and go with him to the hospital, and bring him home after the op, but nothing doing.

'Please don't worry,' said Robin. 'I'll be in and out in just a few days, perhaps two weeks, and then back at Bramblings. They show you how to look after yourself, and then send you home in an ambulance when you're ready.' Typical Rob, to say he didn't need any help from his brother.

'But what about the boys?' Robin's sons had lived with their mother since the divorce. Such had been the animosity of their separation, that I, who was seen by my ex-sister-in-law as part of the enemy camp, had had very little contact.

'It's always difficult, or at least Deborah makes it difficult, to talk to them properly. Last time she sent Charles to stay with me, for the school holidays, he arrived with no luggage whatsoever. My lawyer said that's fairly standard behaviour in these cases. Force you to pay for a new wardrobe. But I'll go down and spend some proper time with them, once I get this thing dealt with.'

'Good idea. I'm due to go up and see Ma in about a month, so call once you know, and tell me what's happening.'

'Of course.' After lunch, Robin headed off to meet friends in Soho, while I walked home through South Kensington. Robin coming home permanently would be great news for Audrie and for his two sons, but clearly he'd need help when he came out of hospital. I remembered the advice our GP had given when I'd started the chemotherapy for leukaemia all those years ago. 'It will be annoying, and boring, some of it will be painful, but in a year it will be over.'

With luck. it would be the same for my brother.

The next day, I dialled Manorfield to tell my mother about our planned holiday.

'I'm so sorry, Mr Sutherland, dear,' responded the manager. 'The doctor's with her, early morning rounds, I can't put you on.'

Mrs Warren was a bustling, friendly soul, strict with her staff but calm and efficient with her clients and patients. She always had time for a chat with residents, and was loved by them and their families.

'And anyway if she could speak now, she wouldn't be able to hear you properly. Your mother's in a bad temper. Her hearing aid is broken. Yesterday she missed *Gardeners' Question Time*.'

'Mrs Warren, thank you. But I've ordered her a new digital one.' This was frustrating. 'The man's supposed to have come and fitted it last week.'

'Did you? She hasn't mentioned it.'

'Never mind. Please let her know I called. I wanted to tell her, we're going to Ceylon – Sri Lanka? She'll be very interested. I'll write her a note about our plans.'

'Of course. Sri Lanka? What a fine thing, I'm sure. She'll be glad to hear you called. One of our carers here is from Sri Lanka.'

That evening I wrote to Audrie, explaining our plan and asking for her suggestions. Her response arrived a few days later, and it contained more than I had expected.

Manorfield House, Milltimber, Aberdeen
Darling Alasdair,
How lovely that you're going back to Ceylon. I'm sure you and Felicity will enjoy the trip, especially if you have time to do a tour up-country. And I'm thrilled Rob is coming home as soon as he's better. But as he says, packing everything up is always so exhausting. I'm pretty feeble at the moment, there's a drip attached to my arm, but after I made a fuss they've put it on the left so I can still write. Here is what you will want to know.
First of all, darling, your father is buried in the Scottish corner of Kanatte Cemetery. His grave is marked with a proper stone.

I never saw it because we'd sailed by the time it was ready,
but they will have the records so if you want, you should
be able to find it.

Our bungalow, Laverstock, was in Melbourne Avenue. In the
evenings, we used often to visit the Garden Club, and of course
your Pa was a member of the Golf and the Rowing Clubs, as
well as all his societies. You might like to stay at the old Galle
Face Hotel. We often went there for dinner dances and parties.
Sometimes we used to drive out to Mount Lavinia for their
Sunday curry lunch and to bathe, it was lovely with a long
beach and palm trees. Or we might stay a night near the beach
at Bentota, and get up very early to watch the turtles.

We were home on leave when the war came, and as soon as we
sailed back, Com joined Colombo Apothecaries. Later on he
was also asked to manage a hotel company up in Kandy, and
often at the weekends we used to motor up to stay at the Queen's
or the Suisse. If he ever had a few days off, we'd go on up to
Nuwara Eliya, where it's so much cooler, stay at the Hill Club
and go for lovely walks. Your grandpa's estate, Glenugie, where
Chim and I grew up, is at Maskeliya, two hours' drive from there.
Darling, that's all I can manage for now. You'll say why didn't
I ever tell you all this before, but when you were little, it never
seemed the right time, and then, all too soon, you weren't here.
I'll get them to post this so it reaches you before you leave.
I do hope to see you soon, and send you all my love.
Ma

All this was new, but I wasn't surprised to be learning it from
a letter. Careful with her words, rationing out her emotions, Audrie
had always found it easier to write about any important issue rather
than speak face to face. Hitherto, she had kept the window on her
own story shut tight. Now, it was open just a crack.

Was it really such a good idea to go back? We both needed
a holiday, but did it have to be Ceylon? Life so far had been happy
and straightforward, admittedly with a couple of wrong turns, but

that was surely normal. Did I really need to add this new dimension? As a Colonial child, sent away to boarding school at seven, what difference would it make to see my birthplace?

It wouldn't matter, I concluded. It would probably be just the same as looking at the old photo albums, except this time in 3D and with a soundtrack.

———————

I closed the door, sat at my desk, flipped through my contacts book and picked up the phone to call the travel agent.

'No, it's not Frankfurt or Milan this time,' I told her. 'It's a holiday. We're thinking of Sri Lanka. Oh, to relax for at least a week or more, and then take a tour, ten days. But I need something special. Could you possible help with some plans?'

'Of course,' she said. 'What do you have in mind?'

I outlined my idea. We discussed the visit for several minutes until, hearing Felicity at the front door, I thanked her and closed the call.

———————

Once he had established himself at Bramblings, Robin called to say that the operation was now scheduled for the end of the following week. He had given my name as next of kin, and the surgeon would telephone immediately after the operation.

'Good luck. We'll be thinking of you,' I said. *'in Bocca al lupo.'*

'Crepi!' came Robin's reply. I put down the phone, relieved that my brother could recall the saying.

When the surgeon called, he said the operation had been difficult and protracted but all was now well and he had confidence that they'd removed all the cancer. I telephoned Audrie, and then my nephews, and Deborah agreed to allow them to visit their father once he was installed at home.

Three days later, we flew up to visit and found him in excellent spirits.

'Apparently they'll let me out towards the end of next week, once I've learned how to handle this embarrassment,' said Rob, pointing to the bag attached to his stomach. 'It'll take some getting used to. I was quite lucky they discovered it early on.' He smiled. 'Serious, but not grave.'

Four days into Robin's recovery, the hospital called again. An infection had set in around the wound and they had, as a precaution, moved Rob from post-op into the intensive care unit. It got quickly worse. The hospital telephoned again the next day. 'He isn't responding so far,' the charge nurse reported. They were doing tests to find out exactly what had happened but the infection had spread to his liver and kidneys.

That same evening we learned that he was being moved by ambulance to a regional critical care unit. The very name was ominous. 'It's a severe sepsis,' I was told. Rob's blood pressure was very low and he'd developed septic shock. They were supporting his breathing, kidney and liver functions, while running tests. 'We still don't know exactly what's caused the problem.'

I felt a sharp pain in my stomach. 'Oh God, how awful. What do you think will happen?'

The doctor wouldn't commit himself. 'We think it's important that you should come.'

I called Audrie to tell her what had happened, promised to be with her next day, and then arranged for my nephews to fly up from Bristol. When Felicity and I arrived at Manorfield, Audrie showed very little emotion, and for a long while gazed in silence out of the window as she thought about the news. Her hand gripped the edge of her chair, white with tension. 'Is it really that bad?' she turned to me, begging for a glimmer of hope.

There was nothing to say which might provide one. Once again, she was hiding her emotions.

I had no idea if she wanted to cry, or hug me, or what.

I could only say, 'It seems so. They still don't know how he developed the infection. It might even be that horrible hospital bug.'

'Frightful. I read about it last year.' She shut her eyes and took a deep breath, as though forcing herself to take in the implications. 'We'll just have to wait and hope. Would you like some tea?' I'd tried as best I could to reassure her, but I knew that it could hardly be worse. We had to go.

'We'll let you know as soon as there's any news.'

Before we set off, Felicity informed the care staff, and called on Audrie's neighbour, asking if she'd be able to pop in to sit with her. At the car door, when I turned to look back, my mother was still in her big armchair by the window, staring out at her garden.

At the infirmary, we waited downstairs for Tom and Charles, and when they arrived from the airport in a taxi, warned them that their father's condition was very serious. The boys, both already as tall as me, nodded sombrely. We took the lift together to the seventh floor of the CCU. At the reception desk, the news was no better.

'We're still not sure. We take every precaution,' the charge nurse explained, rather shamefaced, 'but there's always the possibility that an infection can develop after an operation.' She showed us to a family waiting area. 'And I should warn you, it'll be a bit of a shock.'

When she led our small party into an anteroom with a big glass wall, through which we could see Robin's bed, all four of us were indeed horrified at the sight. What we could see of his face was purple. Tubes emerged all over his body, a drip was fastened to his arm, and an oxygen mask covered his nose.

'Can we go in and be with him?' Tom reached for the door handle.

'No, I'm sorry.' The nurse gripped his arm firmly and pulled him back. 'You can see him, but I'm afraid, not go in. The infection may be highly contagious, so I'm sorry to say that for all your sakes, it's best to stay away.' We stared at Robin for several minutes as the ramifications of what we saw sank in.

We returned, silent now, to the waiting room. 'Will you be staying in the area?' the nurse asked.

'Yes, I will,' I confirmed, 'but I'll speak to the boys' mother, they may have to get back later today. Should we stay?'

I looked at their pale young faces and knew that there was nothing I could say to comfort them. I put an arm around Charles's shoulders, and Felicity, quickly supportive, took Tom's hand.

'I'm afraid we can only ask you to wait for news. I'll be in touch every few hours as it develops,' the nurse assured us, 'and we're doing everything we can.'

Felicity and I sat with our nephews and talked about their options. If they weren't allowed to talk to their father or even be with him, it might be better to go home and wait for news, and come back as soon as he improved. There was no easy option. We took the boys back to the airport, promising to keep them informed, and after checking them in, returned to the hotel.

Two days later, the call came that Robin had died. The official cause of death would be given as septicaemia, they said. Given the unusual circumstances, there would be an autopsy, and they had already called a firm of undertakers to take the body as soon as the procedure had been completed.

'Poor Robin, but poor darling Audrie,' Felicity said. 'It must be the worst thing in the world, to lose an adult child, at that age. When your children are supposed to be there for you for your last few years. It's the wrong order of things.'

When we drove over to tell Audrie, she was resigned and expressionless, and had obviously expected the worst. It seemed that for her, Robin's death had been a foregone conclusion after she'd heard about the infection. Maybe she remembered losing friends that way, so quickly and unexpectedly, in the days before penicillin.

'Two months ago, I hadn't seen him for years,' she said, sadly. 'Then he was back, and no sooner home than off to the hospital. Now, he's gone again. I almost wish he'd never come. He wrote such lovely letters from America, and it was so nice to look forward to seeing him again. I had such happy memories of you two growing up.' She sighed and shut her eyes for a while. 'But it's no good looking back. Can I have a whisky?'

'Of course, Ma. We can't go back. But he was very proud of the boys.'

When I spoke to my nephews again, I kept my tone as matter of fact as possible. Not having seen their father often in the past fifteen years, Tom and Charles might not miss his physical presence, much as I had never missed my own father. But equally, they would miss the idea of a father. They had hardly ever enjoyed the relationship every boy should have with his Pa. Like me, they would wonder later on, what could have been different if he'd survived. But I promised myself, when they asked questions about their father, I would always be there and ready to answer them.

At Bramblings, I found my brother's personal file, which contained his will. It left everything to his two sons and asked me to be his executor. 'Absolutely no religious or any other service of any kind,' Robin had insisted. He wanted the simplest possible cremation. 'No announcements. No flowers, no speeches. Just ask them to get on with it.'

'Shall I come?' Felicity asked ten days later as Tom, Charles and I set out for the crematorium.

'I'm not sure why, but I think we'd better do this on our own,' I responded. 'Just the three of us.'

Afterwards, I realised that to have no funeral formalities had been a huge mistake. My brother had thought only that he didn't want any fuss, but funerals aren't for the benefit of the dead, but to give a chance for the living to say goodbye. This had not been the way to do it.

We had followed the coffin into the crematorium, and taken places in the front row. With just the three of us and the official, the room seemed vast and the coffin incredibly lonely. I stood between my two nephews, with an arm around each. The official looked across at me, and I shook my head. The boys were restless. In the absence of any protocol, none of us knew what to do.

'Let's close our eyes and say goodbye for a minute,' I whispered.

I shut my eyes and put my chin on my chest. For some reason I couldn't understand, I remembered Robin in white shorts and shirt, winning the high jump at school. After the silence, I looked up and signalled for the official to go ahead. The curtains around the pedestal were drawn and the coffin began to move. In the silence, we could hear the movement of the curtain and the machinery which slid the coffin away.

Charles turned to us. 'Let's get out of here.' His face was very pale. We walked quickly out of the building and stood together by the car. I put my arms round Tom and then in turn around his younger brother. We hugged each other. Suddenly we were all weeping, and it took several minutes to recover.

'We never said a proper goodbye,' Tom murmured. 'We should have said something. I know he didn't want it but we should have.' We drove back in silence, while I pondered. Had Robin asked for no funeral or fuss just because he didn't want to give anyone the sorry task of organising it? After a lifetime of being the capable older brother, Robin would have resented the idea of me doing anything for him, and he certainly wouldn't have given the task to his young sons.

Since the seventies, I'd not been close to my brother, and had hardly seen him for nearly twenty years, so I knew I would be less affected by his death than Audrie or the boys. With Robin gone, I was now head of the Sutherland family. Having no children of my own, I would do my best to help my nephews grow into responsible adults.

But until I knew more about my own father, the family portrait would remain out of focus.

———————

Our flight touched down at Colombo at dawn. Even at that hour, the air reeked of rotting vegetation combined with jet fuel. As we emerged from arrivals, we saw a small man in a white shirt and dark grey flannels, waving a sign. As we approached, he smiled broadly, thrust out his hand and introduced himself as Freddie Fernando from Quickshaws.

Fernando led us out into the early morning heat and saw us into an elderly Datsun, introducing the driver as George. He waited while George loaded our bags into the boot, and then jumped into the front.

As we headed into the traffic, Freddie turned completely around in the front seat to face his new visitors. 'You are liking aircon, please?'

'We certainly are, thank you,' I replied. Freddie dutifully waved a hand at the driver. A fan started to wheeze.

'I am so sorry, I forgot,' Freddie beamed. 'On behalf of all of us at Quickshaws, welcome to our country.' During the drive, Freddie put up a constant chatter. There was many unmissable Sri Lankan sights, he asserted, which most distinguished honourable visitors such as Mr Sutherland and the lady would doubtless enjoy. But already hot, and unsettled, I found it hard to pay attention, and looked out of the window. The first indication of the recent civil war was a military roadblock. Young soldiers with rifles stood around, watching us from behind walls of sandbags, while a sentry inspected the inside of the car, before waving us on.

'Mr Sutherland, Madam, have you been here before?' Freddie span around again from the front seat.

'No, Freddie,' replied Felicity. 'This is my first time in Sri Lanka.' She turned to me and tilted her head, grinning.

I was silent for a few moments. 'Yes,' I murmured to myself, 'I've been here before.' But Fernando was already telling us that it would be half an hour's drive. As we crawled through the traffic approaching the city, trees and jungle gradually gave way to more and more small buildings, while on the road, ancient buses billowed smoke, competing for space with mopeds, bicycles, animals and crowds of pedestrians, jostling and hooting and elbowing each other to make their way through the throng. Alongside businessmen in chauffeur-driven cars, there were women carrying small children on one hip, and men naked but for a loincloth, while occasional bullock carts occupied the middle of the road. Everybody seemed to drive at random, using their horns continuously to urge animals, people and other traffic out of the way.

After a maze of turns through city streets, and then down tree-lined suburban avenues, the car finally drew up outside a large white bungalow, surrounded by tall plants and trees. Freddie jumped out and announced, 'I will inform our director, Miss de Mel, of your arrival,' and ran up to the house.

A few moments later, a woman in a beautiful sari appeared in the doorway, introduced herself as Nirmala de Mel, the owner of Quickshaws and led us through the dark, cool interior to a veranda facing the garden, where a table was laid for breakfast.

As soon as we were settled, a servant appeared, offering juices, papaya and mango, and pouring tea. 'Freddie will take you on later to Mount Lavinia,' Nirmala announced as she rejoined us, 'where you must relax completely.'

She took us through her proposed itinerary. After a week's rest, we would stay three nights in Colombo at the old Galle Face Hotel. From there, we'd drive around the city for a day, visit Com's grave at Kanatte Cemetery, perhaps manage some shopping in the Pettah bazaar, and the next day, set out on our tour. After the slow climb to Kandy we would stay at the Queen's Hotel and look in for a meal at the Hotel Suisse, the two that Audrie told us Com had run. Then, we'd move on to the old Hill Station, Nuwara Eliya, and then to Maskeliya, the Finch Noyes' old tea estate in the highlands.

The briefing over, Nirmala asked me if I'd mind helping her to reach down an old Ceylon guide from a high shelf. 'It dates from the thirties when the Sutherlands were here,' she told Felicity. 'It'll be the kind of book Alasdair's mother would have owned.' I left the table and followed her through the house to a well-stocked library, where she pointed to the guidebook on an old Dutch blanket box. She closed the door.

'All fixed for Saturday,' she murmured. 'The agenda will be delivered to you today at the hotel.'

I picked up the guidebook, flipped through, and replaced it. 'Well done, what a relief. And you will come? What about Brian and Heather Lawrence?'

'They will be there,' Nirmala reassured me. 'Very flattered to be asked. Looking forward to seeing you again. Now get back outside to her.'

After breakfast, we set out with Freddie and the driver to Mount Lavinia, the former governor's residence a few miles south of Colombo, now a grand hotel. This, Audrie's letter had said, was where she and Com had often swum and enjoyed Sunday curry lunches.

It was a large white building, perched on a promontory at the edge of a long beach. The car swept into a wide courtyard, with a fountain playing at the centre, and two men in white ran out from the gigantic portico to take our luggage. In the centre of the lobby, a huge wooden fan rotated ponderously.

'I wish we could find something like that on the Portobello Road,' Felicity observed, as the receptionist led us under it and across to the old lift, its glass panes gleaming between gold panels. We watched as it slowly descended to ground level, making a high whining noise, until finally stopping with a long sigh as the gilded gates clanked open.

Quickshaws had booked us a room in the old wing, where the charm of the Colonial decor did not quite make up for the age of the furnishings, but it was appealing, with a huge four-poster bed. Once unpacked, and settled, we came downstairs and emerged onto to the pool terrace, choosing a table overlooking the sea, in the shade of a tall palm. We sat, quietly unwinding, watching the breakers of the Indian Ocean across the long beach. For me, there was something very comforting about lounging on a terrace at Mount Lavinia, enjoying a proper Ceylon curry and rice, with a few Elephant beers, just as my father must have done so many times. After the overnight flight and a long day, it was soon time for sleep.

On the next afternoon, following a good lunch during which we had both sampled the local Arrack spirit, we returned to sunbathe and snooze by the pool. I decided that the time was perfect. If not now, then when?

'Darling, have you brought anything smart to wear?'

Felicity looked up sharply from her book.

'What? Don't say we've got to get dressed up. I've brought some black silk trousers and a white Kurta. What on earth for?'

'That'll be ideal, darling, perfect. Well, I've arranged for us to get married. On Saturday. Up at the Galle Face.'

Felicity's eyes widened. 'What on earth?'

I'd expected her to be thrilled. But for the next half an hour she stamped around the pool, drank several more glasses of Arrack brandy, and cursed me loudly that she had been trapped. Eventually

I got up and walked round next to her. Other guests and several staff watched as we circled.

'What's the matter? Why are you so upset? You've always said you would. Marry me, I mean.' I confessed that I'd enlisted Nirmala's help to make all the arrangements. Felicity's assistant had even found the necessary documents, a copy of her birth certificate and her divorce papers.

'What? Suzie knew all along? The traitor. Or traitress.'

'Don't blame her. She knew it would be a good idea. And you did say yes, plenty of times.'

Felicity stopped abruptly and turned to face me, glass in hand. 'Of course I did,' she seethed. 'But I didn't expect to have to do it. We're perfectly happy as we are? Why do you have to interfere? You've got me cornered. I can't let you down and I'm totally unprepared.'

She turned away, tripped, and fell into the pool. I jumped in after her, and when I surfaced I saw, much to my relief, that she was laughing.

On Friday morning, the car arrived to take us in to Colombo. At the Galle Face Hotel, an extremely old man in a spotless coat and turban, with several rows of medals across his chest, came out to greet us, putting his palms together and saying '*Ayubowan*, welcome, Master, welcome, Lady.'

'He looks as though he's been doing that for fifty years,' said Felicity as the door closed behind us.

'More like sixty,' I replied, thinking of Audrie's letter. 'He was probably here to welcome my parents for the Thursday dinner and dance.' We strolled into the reception area, with its marble floor and slow-turning fans overhead. Two elegant sari-clad women made *Ayubowan*, escorted us to the check-in. When we spotted a 'This Week's Events' sign in the lobby reading *Sutherland Wedding, 12 PM Saturday. Ballroom*, Felicity insisted on asking one of the receptionists to photograph us in front of it.

We were shown into a gigantic room on the second floor in the old part of the hotel. It was twenty yards' walk from the bed to the bathroom door. 'Big enough for a squash court,' Felicity noted. When

I turned on the water for a shower, there came the distant noise of pipes shuddering, which grew slowly louder until finally a trickle of water appeared. It was cold. I rang the service bell, and less than five seconds later, there was a soft tap at the door. An elderly moustachioed steward in a white uniform introduced himself as Edmond, our room boy. 'No water,' I explained. Edmond hurried across to the bathroom. There was a tapping of metal on metal, a loud gurgling noise, and a few minutes later he re-emerged, smiling.

"Hot water is coming now, thank you. May I bring you any cold drink?' He pattered away down the corridor.

'This is what it must have been like for your people,' Felicity laughed, 'life surrounded by servants. Very eighteenth century.'

Nirmala arrived to join us for lunch, dying to know how her plans had worked out. After Felicity had berated her for 'treachery and cunning', she invited her to be her witness and bridesmaid for the ceremony. Because I had been born in Colombo, Nirmala explained, there had been no problems of establishing Sri Lankan residency before we could be married. Everything was all set for the wedding.

At eleven thirty the following day, Nirmala reappeared, this time behind a huge bunch of frangipani for Felicity. She was soon followed by Brian Lawrence, a business friend from my Hong Kong days, and his wife, Heather, whereupon Brian immediately marched us all to the bar area and ordered champagne. Our small wedding party sat on ornate chairs in the corner of the bar, toasting each other, until twenty minutes later, a dusty Toyota arrived at the front. The registrar, a small untidy man in a grey shirt, hopped out, accompanied by a colleague. Nirmala went out to greet him and brought them inside.

'This is most unusual,' the official frowned, 'and most inconvenient. Definitely not in accordance with regulations solemnising marriage outside Registrar's office, Section 38(1).'

Nirmala stepped forward. 'You've been very well paid, Mr Wicknamaratne. May I suggest we get on with it?'

There was sheepish Sri Lankan head bobbing. He followed her across the lobby, the rest of the party behind, to a pair of double doors, marked **Grand Ballroom**, and guarded by a liveried bellboy.

'The Sutherland wedding party,' Nirmala announced grandly.

'Oh, yes, madam, please to follow me.' He threw the doors open, reached for a bank of switches just inside the door and the vast room filled with light from a dozen chandeliers. It was empty except for a long table at the centre, covered with flowers and with two chairs on either side.

'My God, Nirmala,' gasped Felicity as she turned slowly to take it all in. 'How on earth did you fix this?'

Feeling somewhat lonely in such space, Felicity and I sat opposite Mr Wicknamaratne as his assistant handed him the registration forms. He slowly read out the formal wedding proceedings in Sinhala and then English, before handing Felicity a pen and indicating where we should sign. Nirmala, and then Brian and Heather Lawrence witnessed our signatures, and the assistant folded the documents into his briefcase for processing. It was done.

'We will send copy to British High Commission,' the registrar informed them. 'Are you requiring notarised English translation of the certificate?'

'Certainly we are, thank you,' I answered.

'That will be fifty rupees. Delivered to hotel tomorrow.'

I paid him, and the new Mr & Mrs Sutherland led our friends back to the bar. Mr Wicknamaratne, now rather less grumpy, declined my offer of a drink, saying he must return to his office. As we followed him outside, a photographer appeared from the hotel lobby. Nirmala had thought of everything.

That evening, the festivities over and our friends now departed, we telephoned to tell our families and friends the news of our marriage, and invite them all to a party in London in a few weeks' time. Later, we sat on our balcony in the dusk, watching the fishermen, balanced on their stilts a hundred yards out to sea, waiting patiently for a last catch.

'I'm so glad we were able to have it in the Galle Face,' I said. 'This old hotel's almost in our blood. We're the third generation here. I'm so glad you finally gave in.'

'It was perfect, darling, impossibly romantic, so beautifully done,' Felicity said, as we prepared for bed. 'Just us in that huge room. Not a hat in sight.'

Later, I awoke to Felicity tugging my shoulder. 'Wake up, wake up, listen, there's someone here!' There was a grinding sound which seemed to come from near the bedroom door. I crept over and quickly pulled it open. Edmond, our room boy, lay fast asleep on a canvas truckle bed, snoring to raise the dead.

On Monday morning, notebook in hand, I asked George, the driver, to take us first to the cemetery at Kanatte.

The wizened custodian looked up Robert William Sutherland in his burials book for 1946, and slowly led us past a century of headstones,to Com's resting place. Having brought us to the grave, the old boy knelt down and brushed away the worst of the lichen and moss which covered the stone, before stepping back a discreet ten yards. Felicity squeezed my hand, and announced she would take a little walk.

I stood alone, looking at my father's name carved on the stone, wondering what he would make of me now. We didn't know each other, I thought, but I hope you'd have been proud of me. Of how Audrie brought us up without you. And of your new daughter-in-law.

I'd often wondered what type of man my father had been, what had made Audrie fall for him, and how his early death must have changed her. Back in England, as a widow, she had tried to be both mother and father to us, as far as it was possible. But how different one's life would have been if Com had been there all along. One would probably be a much better person all round.

How terrible it was, for Audrie, all those years ago, standing right here, watching her husband's body buried, as was the regulation in every hot country, less than twenty-four hours after he had died. Her letter said she'd never seen the stone, so I decided to take a picture for her, and have the grave tidied up. I paid the guardian for the cleaning, and said we'd be back in a few days to see the result.

'Are you OK?' asked Felicity, once we were back in the car. 'You were there for quite a while.'

'Yes, I was miles away, thinking about Audrie standing here while he was buried. It seems so un-oriental, just like a cemetery in Scotland. I'm sorry to take you to graveyards on our honeymoon,' I apologised. 'But…'

'Don't be silly,' she laughed. 'It's you and me. Everything else is the same. Just let's do the holiday exactly we planned. Except now we can sign the hotel register as Mr & Mrs.'

As George drove us slowly around Colombo, many street and building names seemed familiar – Cinnamon Gardens, the Pettah, the Fort, York Street. The main shop of the Colombo Apothecaries was still there, on the corner of York and Princes streets, but Steuart Place had become a complex of arcades and hotels.

At Laverstock, Com and Audrie's bungalow in Melbourne Avenue, where I'd been somehow expecting to see ghosts of lives past, we were greeted by a secretary from the new occupier, the Colombo Plan Bureau, who insisted on showing us around the entire house. Although there were still many original features, doorways and the beautiful carved wooden stair-rail, all the grander rooms had been divided up by cheap partitions. We stood on the rear veranda, where Audrie and Com had enjoyed the cooler early mornings and evenings. It was easy to imagine their lives in that house, the sounds of family life, of children, of parties and dinners and gossip and friends. But outside, the garden was derelict and forgotten.

The road up to Kandy twisted around dizzying turns through terraces of tea rising up into the clouds, flanked by waving palms and huge waterfalls which tumbled into the jungle below. Swarms of little boys scrambled up the hillside to knock on the car window asking for 'School Pen?' and then, as the driver swung them into another hairpin, the same shining faces appeared fifty yards further up the hill, on the other side of the car, with the same message. George leaned over and handed out biros into their waiting hands. 'We are always coming prepared,' he laughed.

We stopped on the road below Kandy, where sacks of rice had fallen from a lorry, and a nearby wild elephant had caught the scent; for some time it charged about in the jungle, furiously trumpeting and challenging some village boys, who in turn banged and clattered kettles and pans in an attempt to frighten it off. When the driver sensed a lull in the proceedings, he hurriedly drove us on and away, before the elephant re-emerged from the jungle to stake its claim.

At Kandy, we checked into the Queen's Hotel. Felicity had brought my copy of George Skeen's *A Guide to Kandy*, published in 1903, and when we reached our room, she read out:

> *Overlooking the lake is the Queen's Hotel, a Hotel of the highest class, occupying the best site in the town with a view of esplanade, lake, mountains, and the great Buddhist Temple. Its carriages and porters meet all trains. It possesses two large drawing rooms, a billiard room with three good tables, and suites of private sitting rooms provided with electric light and fans.*

Not much had changed. Ours was a large room on the corner, with a balcony facing the lake and looking up the road towards the Temple of the Tooth. There were vast fans and gleaming marble and parquet floors and it was easy to imagine the hotel as it had been when Mr Skeen wrote his guide, or when Com had run the company forty years later. We walked around the lake to look at the Hotel Suisse, and then dined in the Queen's vast pillared restaurant with its chandeliers, and waiters moving as slowly and silently as the turning fans.

The Queen's certainly wasn't luxury anymore, but slightly threadbare and quite expensive. But to me, it felt unchanged, and there, of all the places I'd read about in his letters so far, I felt the closest to my father.

The next day, after passing Edinburgh, to a chorus of chattering monkeys, we finally arrived at Nuwara Eliya. To finish climbing at last, and emerge onto the long, flat green plateau was an extraordinary transformation. The air felt fresh, the temperature ten degrees cooler, as we arrived at the Hill Club, a low stone building with mullioned windows, which resembled an ageing Highland shooting lodge.

'It's perfectly preserved,' Felicity observed, 'like an echo of Victorian Ceylon.'

This, I'd told Felicity, was also where my parents had spent the first few days of their honeymoon. In the bar, next to stuffed and mounted stags' heads, we found boards listing officers of the club in the twenties and thirties, and there, sure enough, was engraved the name of my grandfather, and Finch's great friends, Ham Mann and Charlie Burrows.

Upstairs in the bedroom, a one-bar electric heater glowed faintly in the fireplace, just like the ones my mother had finally thrown away when she installed central heating in 1960. A faded old pink quilted eiderdown lay on the bed, with weights hanging down on either side to keep it in place.

Felicity jumped on it with glee. 'Now all I need is a gigantic hot water bottle, and I'm not moving.'

On our walk the next morning, we felt as though we were wandering through a rural British 1930s film set. The red-brick post office featured a Roman clock face, there was Victoria Park, the racecourse, the golf course, and neat rows of bungalows with roses and rows of vegetables. Here, up-country, it seemed nothing much had changed in the half-century since Audrie had taken her final passage home.

We set out early the following morning, and drove through the Central Highlands, past Hatton, via Maskeliya and Glenugie, the tea estate where my grandfather had lived and worked for twenty years, the names constantly suggesting that we were touring the North East of Scotland – Dalhousie, Faithlie and Strathdon led on to Aberdeen.

Returning finally to Colombo, I asked the driver to take us back to Kanatte Cemetery. The stone had been cleared of its fifty years of moss and lichen. I paid the guardian, took some more photographs, and stood once again for several minutes by the grave. Now that we had seen where Com and Audrie lived and worked, and absorbed the atmosphere, I would read all of the letters, and be able to understand Com and Audrie's lives, maybe even what had really happened.

The following weekend, back in London, I telephoned Audrie and my nephews again, while Felicity called her own family, to tell them about the wedding and tour. 'About time too,' Audrie laughed.

Felicity was a welcome addition to the family, she said, and would I please bring her up as soon as possible.

Once unpacked, I made up an album of photographs of the holiday, and sent it to her with a note to say we'd followed her advice about the tour.

A few months later came the call which I'd been half-expecting. Audrie was weaker, the care manager said. They had moved her from her little flat into a nursing room upstairs, and it might be wise to come soon.

I took an early flight up to Aberdeen, rented a car, and drove out towards Milltimber. Manorfield was a collection of modern two-storey buildings, set into the hillside, in the ubiquitous creamy stone and with a grey slate roof, and surrounded by newly laid lawns.

I stood at the door of Audrie's room. The October sun was streaming in and through the wide window I could see over the trees and across the valley to the river. Audrie was dozing, with a copy of *The Times* lying across her chest. There was an untouched cup of tea on the side table, by the bunch of asters I'd sent nearly a week ago. On the chest of drawers were the familiar photographs, the 1938 wedding portrait, one of my six-year-old brother with our father, standing outside the house in Colombo, and Audrie's favourite photo of me, aged eighteen.

'Hello, Ma, how are you?' I said gently. She opened her eyes and smiled. I bent to kiss her.

'Hello, darling. What a lovely surprise.' She pushed herself up, and coughed, three or four times, a dry, short cough. 'How are you? Sorry I'm a bit feeble, not sure why, Harding says it's my chest. Frankly I don't understand what's happening. I'd like to get back downstairs to my flat.' Her pale blue eyes sparkled, belying her tired voice. She wore a warm bedjacket over her nightgown, and an Alice Band held her silver hair back from her lined face. As she pulled the blanket, the familiar Ceylon sapphire and diamond engagement ring shone on her left hand.

'Why are you here?' Audrie asked.

'I had to go and see Clark & Wallace about selling the house,' I lied, 'so I thought I'd drop in and see how you are. Mrs Warren said Dr Harding was coming by this evening, and she'll give me a progress report. We can have lunch together.' I wondered if that sounded reassuring.

I helped her sit up properly, plumped up the pillows and re-arranged the bedcovers. Then, I sat by her and held her hand, while we discussed the home, the nurses, family, children, cousins, and eventually, the food. Audrie always complained about the food.

'It's not bad. Lunch can be all right, at least the plates are warm. But not the sort of lunch I like. Too mushy. Dinner's much better, but the one thing I hate is that in the evening they feed us at six thirty,' she complained. 'It's because the kitchen staff go off duty at seven. But who can eat at six thirty? It's not even yet time for a whisky.'

'Shall I tell you about the Sri Lanka tour?' I looked around the room for the photo album I'd sent her.

'Of course, darling, but not now. What's happening in London, have you seen cousin Virginia?'

I knew that I must try again. "Ma, can I ask you something? It's been bothering me. I know it's probably not a good time, but there never seems to be a good time.'

She looked up at me rather nervously. 'What is it?'

'About my Pa. We went to see his grave at Kanatte, and I wondered, what happened when he died?'

Her eyes widened and her voice tightened. 'Oh, please don't ask me to talk about that!' She shut her eyes, took a breath, and coughed several times. When she spoke again a long time later, it was in a calm, quiet tone.

'Can't you understand? Must I spell it out? It was the most terrible thing imaginable, the worst ever, and I've never stopped thinking about it. Thinking what I could have done. Should have done.'

She gave a long sigh and lay back on her pillow. It had been a mistake to ask.

'Ma, I'm sorry, it's all right. Don't worry.'

There was a long silence. Audrie slid further down into the bed.

'Darling, it's lovely to see you. I'm going to rest, why don't you come back later when Dr Harding will be here, and you can ask her what's the matter with me and how long I'll have to stay up here, and then you can tell me.'

'Are you sure? I'm very happy to sit and chat. Or I could just stay here and read while you snooze?' I noticed a comfortable-looking armchair by the window. 'I can sit there and look at your lovely view.'

'Don't be silly. Of course, you don't want to sit here indoors on a sunny day like this.' She had clearly forgotten her anger, or wanted to. 'Go and have lunch, go for a walk, or why not go down to the Deeside and play some golf? You probably need the exercise. I'll see you later.' She shut her eyes again and prepared to sleep.

Golf? She was right, I could do with some fresh air. I watched as she quickly fell asleep, then closed her door, walked down the two flights to reception, and drove back towards Aberdeen, turning off to the Deeside Golf Club. In the Pro shop, I borrowed a putter and a pitching wedge, and spent an hour on the practice ground, turning over all the time what news the doctor might have, and what I should say if it was as bad as they feared.

When I drove back to Manorfield, Dr Harding was walking into the building. It was still bright and sunny but now there was an autumn chill in the air. Inside, we stood back as an elderly patient was wheeled past into the lift. The lift door opened and Dr Harding led the way along the corridor into a small side room, offered me a chair and took one herself.

'I saw my mother this morning,' I said. 'She seems in reasonable form.'

'Yes, she's in surprisingly good spirits.'

'Surprisingly? What exactly is wrong with her?'

Dr Harding leaned forward, and I knew it wasn't going to be good.

'I've seen the tests. I'm sorry, it's not welcome news. There's a large tumour on her lung. It's not at all good, I'm afraid. But she's not in any pain, which is a comfort.'

'A tumour. Cancer?'

'Yes, inoperable at her age, I'm afraid.'

I wondered how to react to news like this. I'd known it was coming. She must suspect. I wasn't surprised, but what should I say? Why did I think of Camus and *L'Étranger*?

The doctor interrupted my thoughts.

'How much was she smoking?'

'Recently? Not at all. She gave up a few years ago, quite by accident, after fifty years of non-stop.' I wondered why she'd asked. 'You remember she contacted meningitis, and was in a coma for ten days?'

'Yes, I do recall. We thought for a while, that was it. But she's a tough old girl. How did she manage to stop?' She watched me expectantly, as though anticipating a secret.

'More than tough. When she recovered, I came up again to take her home.' I remembered driving her home in a rental car. 'I joked in the car that because of the coma, she already hadn't smoked for three weeks, so she'd got through the worst part. When she realised what had happened, she decided that was it, and never touched another. But she'd been smoking since the war.'

Harding wrote some notes on a pad. A nurse knocked on the door, looked in, said, 'Sorry,' and closed it again.

'Well, she's very frail now,' the GP continued, 'we haven't told her, but the tumour is growing, and at her age there's no point in treating it or operating. We'll watch her and make sure she's comfortable and in no pain. It could be a few weeks or even a few days. I'm sorry we can't be more optimistic.'

I paused. This was what I'd expected, but it was still a shock. 'There's no sense in trying chemo? Or is it too late?'

'We discussed this, of course,' she replied. 'But it would take a long course of therapy to have any effect on this size of tumour, and it would make her very uncomfortable. We don't advise it, I hope you understand.'

'Thank you for being so honest. She was worrying about what was keeping her in bed. Does she know what's happening?'

'She's a clever woman and there's nothing wrong with her mind. She must know we brought her upstairs to the nursing rooms for a good reason, not just a cough.'

'You're right.' I realised what Audrie was up to. She probably knew, but didn't want to discuss it, and it would be typical of her to shield me from bad news. She had never talked about bad news, but usually waited until it went away.

'I won't mention it. I'll tell her it's her chest, but there's no need to worry. And I can come back up at the weekend.'

We shook hands, and I walked slowly back down to my mother's room. If I told her she was OK, what if my face betrayed that I wasn't telling the truth? I didn't want to tell her the end was near, but ought I really to keep it from her? Felicity's mother had insisted that her daughter should stay with her when she knew her end was near – she didn't want to die alone. But Audrie, more private, would be less likely to want me there. What did I want to do? I couldn't sit around and wait for weeks in case she suddenly worsened. I had to get back to London, do some work and let nature take its course.

The corridor was very quiet, everything seemed so ordered, so calm. There were pictures of Balmoral and Deeside on the walls.

'Ma?' She was awake and smiled, trying again to push herself up on the pillows. 'I've seen Melissa Harding, Ma, and you were right, she says it's your chest. Not too good. A legacy of that smoking.'

'Too many Du Mauriers and Bensons.' She coughed again.

'Wasn't it Passing Clouds that Grandpa used to smoke? They were so strong, and untipped. What can I get you, some water? A cup of tea?'

'Well… my first-ever cigarette was a Player's Navy Cut, on board ship, nearly sixty years ago. Is it too early for a glass of something? Let's have a whisky.'

'You're allowed whisky?'

'At my great age, I can have what I want. Kay brought me some. In the cupboard.' She waved at the sideboard.

Inside was a bottle of Standfast, and some old Waterford tumblers which I recognised. I poured us each a small tot, added a little water from the carafe by her bedside, and handed her a glass. She raised it with a tired smile. 'Chin-chin.'

'To you, darling Ma, and a swift return downstairs to your flat.'

We touched the glasses together.

'And to you, darling. Thank you for coming up.' We sipped the whisky and I helped her replace the glass on the bedside table.

'I'm going to stay up tonight, I'll beg a bed with the Garlands and come to see you again tomorrow.' Kay Garland had been a friend of Audrie's since before the war.

'Tomorrow? Nonsense.' She motioned as if to send me away. 'You've work to do, darling, I'm sure. Come next week. Sandy and Adrian will drop in tomorrow.' The Hamiltons were Audrie's former neighbours, loyal friends who had always kept an eye on her.

'Are you sure?' I crossed to the other side of the bed to look at the photographs on the table.

'Of course. And what would you do but sit?'

'We could chat.'

'I'm a little too tired to talk much. No, off you go, darling.'

'If you're sure.'

'Off back to London,' she smiled. 'And Felicity.'

'All right. If you insist.' I bent over and kissed her forehead. 'Goodbye, Ma, see you in a few days.'

'Darling.' She waved a frail hand at me. I watched her shut her eyes, took the empty glasses and washed them in her bathroom sink. At the door, I checked her again before leaving the room, but she was already dozing. Downstairs at reception, Mrs Warren was talking to a middle-aged couple near the front door. She signalled to me, asking to have a word, and walked over.

'Goodbye, Mr Sutherland, Dr Harding advised me. I'm sorry to hear the news isn't so good. But we will make sure she's comfortable.'

'Thank you, Mrs Warren.' We shook hands. I wondered why, as we'd not done so before.

'I'll be back in a few days. She's sleeping again now.'

'We'll call if there's any change.' I started having second thoughts. What if this was the last time I ever saw her?

'D'you think I should stay nearby? It'd be no problem, we have friends in Banchory.'

'Don't worry about staying here, Mr Sutherland,' the manager reassured me. They would keep a close eye on her and let me know straight away if there was any change.

'It was no good,' I told Felicity when I got home. 'Just asking her about my Pa put her into a spin. I think she must feel guilty about something to do with his death. Maybe that she could have saved him, I don't know.'

I hadn't played my cards very well, going straight in with the question.

'She didn't want to talk, even suggested I should go and play golf. And when I said I'd stay overnight, she wasn't having it. She sent me back to you. Typical.'

Now that I'd had a couple of hours to think about it, I was beginning to wish I had after all invited myself to stay nearby with Kay Garland, instead of taking Audrie at her word to come back down to London. Felicity tried to comfort me.

'She would never have known where you were, would she?'

'No,' I responded. 'But as Mrs Warren said, she wasn't dumb, she knew she was ill and had probably faced the idea that she hadn't long to go.'

'Shouldn't you have told her?'

'Dr Harding advised not. But she wouldn't want to discuss it with me of all people. It would be just like her to want to cope with it alone, and send me away. She's always shielded me from any bad news, think of the burglary.'

Five years before, Audrie had been robbed while she was asleep, but never mentioned it to me, and coped with it all herself. I'd only discovered when on a visit, months later, I noticed the empty space in her drawing room where an antique inlaid tallboy had stood.

'I remember,' Felicity nodded. 'Didn't they find it for sale in the antique shop?'

The phone rang.

'Mr Sutherland, it's Angela Warren at Manorfield.'

'Yes?' I shivered. I reached out a hand and leaned against the wall.

'It's your mother. I'm afraid she's gone. Just half an hour ago. I'm so sorry.'

Audrie must have known, all along, I now knew for certain. She'd made sure I wasn't there when it happened.

'Are you there?' Mrs Warren's voice brought me back with a jolt. 'We went in to check on her, she seemed to be asleep, she hadn't eaten anything, but then she didn't wake up. She had just slipped very quietly away.'

'Thank you, thank you, Mrs Warren,' I said eventually. 'At least I got to see her before she died. What do I need to do?' My eyes lit on the framed photograph of Audrie and Robin on the bookshelf.

'Nothing now, we'll take care of everything. Dr Harding has just been with her. But perhaps you could call in the morning to make the arrangements. Speak to the administrator's office.'

'Yes, of course. Thank you again, Mrs Warren, goodbye.' I found myself wondering how often that kind woman had to make calls like that, and if she ever got used to it. I put down the handset and turned to see Felicity coming out of the kitchen with the wine glasses.

'Here we are. Enough left for a glass each bef…' She stopped. 'But, darling, what's the matter?'

'That was them. It's over. Audrie died half an hour ago.'

'Oh, my darling, I'm so sorry,' she said. 'Are you all right? How did it happen?' She put the glasses down and wrapped her arms round me, and we held each other for a long minute.

'Such an odd day. Now I have no idea what I think. Or feel. I kept remembering Camus, you know, *Mother died today, or it could have been yesterday.*'

Felicity took a sip of the wine. 'How do we react when this happens? Is it easier when one's half-expecting it? Did you think she'd go so quickly?'

'Of course, she must have sent me away to protect me.' I drained the glass and got up to fetch a new bottle from the fridge. 'I don't feel like weeping. It will probably come tomorrow. We can speak to them in the morning and make arrangements.'

'When can the funeral be, d'you think? Do you need to go back to work?' Felicity's voice was soothing. 'Do you want me to speak to the rest of the family, cousins and so on? If you have to travel, I can handle all the arrangements, just let me know.'

'No, darling, thank you, but I'd prefer to do it myself. I'll call Robin's boys and the Finch Noyes cousins.' I opened the wine, poured us both a glass, and raised mine. 'Four hours ago I had a tot with Audrie, and we drank to her swift recovery. Now let's drink to her memory.'

'To Audrie,' said Felicity. We drank the wine. 'Darling, let's come and start dinner. What a day. Typical Audrie to go like that, no fuss.'

'Maybe later,' Audrie had said. Now that she had gone, I could properly investigate the archive of material she had left me.

I dug out the silk bundle again, and spread the contents over the kitchen table. It was an extraordinarily eclectic collection. In addition to airmail letters, all-in-one aerograms, miniature wartime V-mails, and regular letters, there were menus, telegrams, photographs, ship's programmes, press cuttings and several official documents.

Then I paused, wondering if this idea was, after all, for the best. My whole life so far had been presented to me, as if on a series of trays. Prep school, big school, pass exams, go to university, get a job, build a career, save up for a deposit, buy a flat. Nothing so far had emerged which might obstruct a normal, reasonably happy life. Perhaps I'd been very lucky. But if Audrie had always kept this bundle secret, might it contain news I might not want to read?

Two pages torn from a 1954 calendar reminded me about a summer I'd never forgotten. At school in early May, Audrie had written to say, although not in so many words, that she planned to abandon me for the holidays. She would be driving to Athens, she said, with my godmother, her Ceylon friend Gertie. Meanwhile, I would spend the summer at a children's holiday camp.

I stared at the two scruffy pages, which she had torn out and saved, a very dry outline of what must have been an extraordinary adventure. The two women had driven from Dieppe to Athens in ten days, via Strasbourg, Zagreb and Skopje. It seemed typical of her to have kept a brief note of the route, but leave no detail of what actually happened on the trip. Back then there were no motorways, the roads were generally terrible, and the paperwork required for them to make such a journey must have been appalling. I imagined it all in black and white, the era of *The Third Man*. Germany and Austria were a bureaucratic nightmare, still administered by the four Allied powers. Yugoslavia was Communist, not quite a Soviet satellite but not far from it. Audrie and Gertie, however, had both been through wartime sea voyages and London–Athens by road was probably a ten-day picnic.

While Audrie braved the hazards of the Balkans, I'd spent that summer holiday in a large house near the seafront in Angmering. There were about two dozen other children, mostly from Colonial families, including several pairs of siblings, all of us about eight or nine. We slept in dormitories, with the girls on the second floor and the boys under the eaves. Nobody was homesick. There were trips to the beach, expeditions and outings almost every day. The breakfasts were huge, and all the meals ample, which mattered a great deal after so many years of rationing. We drank lashings of Tizer, and I remembered how delicious it was, the only fun drink for children in those days. I was sure I'd had a better time there than I would have had, sitting at home in Sussex.

'So was it,' Felicity asked when I showed her the calendar pages, 'another part of Audrie's grand plan for you and Robin to grow up independent? Or was it her own selfishness?'

'Perhaps she was trying to make me self-reliant,' I said. 'But maybe she just needed a break, to get away and let her hair down, after nine years of bringing up two boys on her own.'

But now, if I was to learn about their life in Ceylon, I'd have to approach it systematically, instead of fiddling about at random. Com's letters would come first. I went through the entire pile and separated all the envelopes in my father's handwriting. The rest went back into two box files, and would have to wait. I put the letters into date order, as far as I could tell what dates they were. There were more than three hundred. Com's early letters to her, from Colombo to addresses up-country, with local stamps, were obviously written when they had just met. Later ones were sent to her on board different ships. A couple of years later, they were addressed to Audrie in South Africa. Why then? Why there? What had happened in South Africa?

I spent the weekend before the funeral dictating a first batch of letters into my laptop. Gradually, I learned how to decipher my father's hand. Seated at the desk, reading them out loud, I lurched from one emotional extreme to the other. Sometimes Com's humour could be very Wodehousian, and his view of the world as a vaguely ridiculous place would make me stop and smile or even laugh. In other letters, a dark mood smoked off the page like a mist. Sometimes, to read his words out loud into the microphone felt very clinical, like a surgeon dissecting the interior of an unfamiliar body, but now and then a passage would unveil another unknown family story, or fill in another piece in the jigsaw, forcing a five-minute break. I would disconnect the headset and walk about the flat for a while. People and place names cropped up, some I now knew, some not. I scribbled them all into a notebook.

The fog which Audrie had cast over their lives began to clear, but still, even after reading fifty letters, there were no clues to reveal why she had never talked about him to me.

Kay Garland, Audrie's oldest friend, would be at her funeral; I'd ask her.

———————————

Returning to Manorfield, I arranged for the removal of Audrie's few remaining possessions. The staff had tidied up her room, everything had been packed, and there were no traces of her ever being there. I stood by the window for a moment, remembering that last visit on the day she'd died. The books, I would keep, and her clothes could go to the Aberdeen Instant Neighbour charity, long one of her favourite causes.

As I prepared to leave, Mrs Warren invited me to step into her office for a moment. She had carefully packed Audrie's handbag, purse and last few remaining personal possessions into two Manorfield carrier bags, which I signed for.

'We all had great respect for your mother,' she told me in her charming Aberdeen burr. 'She was a fine lady, fine, very dignified. And she had a great sense of humour. And that laugh!"

'Thank you,' I replied. 'Yes of course, very kind. She enjoyed her time here. Thank you for everything you did for her.'

'I always liked chatting with her,' Mrs Warren continued. 'She had such an interesting and colourful life. She told me all about life in Ceylon and South Africa, and about her voyages on those wonderful old ships. And being torpedoed! What an amazing adventure! You're very lucky to have had such an interesting mother.'

Torpedoed? This was news to me. South Africa? Would that explain the airmail letters? Why had she been able to tell so much to this kind, caring woman, but not to me, her own child?

Outside, still puzzling, I put the carrier bags on the back seat of the car. At the top of one, I recognised the photograph album I'd sent Audrie of our tour of Sri Lanka, and took it out to look at it again. As I leafed through, I came to the pages where I'd inserted the pictures of my father's grave, taken on the two visits to Kanatte Cemetery. The page was empty. Audrie had removed all the photos of the grave, both before and after its clean-up. So she'd been determined, even in her final days, to make sure she never had to think about it. How on earth could that have still persisted?

I had called Audrie's solicitor, and when I came home her will had appeared in the post. Since my brother's death, a note had been added to the effect that I was her sole heir as well as her executor. The original will, however, contained one more surprise. 'I request my executor,' one clause read, 'to ensure that funds are regularly remitted for birthday and Christmas presents for my daughter, Susan Sutherland, in South Africa.'

So I had a sister! Where? Why had she never told me? Had Robin known? Surely Robin would have known her. Another secret Audrie had never shared. Was Susan still alive? What else was there to discover? I went out and walked around for half an hour, a thousand thoughts and possibilities dancing like pieces of a jigsaw in my mind, but there seemed to be no pattern. Where could I look to find my sister? There would certainly be something about her in that huge pile of letters. Perhaps Kay Garland would know.

I took Kay Garland's arm and led her slowly through the little churchyard to the car, followed by Felicity with Ticia, Kay's daughter.

I'd managed to get through the short service and my eulogy without tears – the actor's tip to douse a hanky with strong smelling salts had helped with that – and even Kay, surely with so many memories of her long friendship with Audrie, had remained stoic. Now, as we made our way back to the Garlands' house, perhaps she would be able to throw some light on Susan, on my father's life and death, and all the mysteries I'd begun to uncover.

The road to the Garlands' house in Banchory was slippery, with occasional clouds of leaves drifting across in the wind. Dark pines leaned overhead, making the route alternately shaded and bright as clouds and then shadows hid and revealed the occasional weak sunshine.

'It was such bleak weather for a funeral,' Ticia said, turning towards me and Felicity in the back. 'But it was lovely, don't you think? I'd no idea she had so many friends up here. The people from Manorfield seemed very caring and fond of her.'

'They were,' I agreed. 'Mrs Warren's an angel. But at those prices, I should think so.' Audrie had lived there for more than a year and it had cost her almost five hundred pounds a week. 'There's nothing left in the account.'

'Are you planning to sell the house?' asked Ticia.

'Yes, as soon as I can,' I nodded.

'You must stay with us next time you're up here,' she offered.

'We'd love to,' Felicity leaned forward. 'Thank you so much.' Until then, she too had been quiet, as we gradually shed the tension of the funeral. 'I know he'd love to have a good natter about Audrie.'

She knew what I was thinking almost before I did myself. The big car slowed down, as Ticia turned sharply left to climb up the brae towards Durris. Halfway up, as the dense roadside forest of silver birches and pines gave way to an elegantly manicured hedge, she turned into a drive where a solid, wide grey stone house sat comfortably surrounded by broad green lawns, facing a view across the valley.

'Here we are, this is home.' Ticia drove into a courtyard and up to the front door. 'Why don't you take Mum on in, and I'll turn the car round.' Kay, magnificent in black Chanel, handed me her stick and put out a gloved hand to steady herself as she stepped down.

Once inside, Kay took off her black hat with its tiny veil. 'Come in and let's sit,' she said. 'Mrs Fraser will be somewhere, she'll make us some tea, unless you'd like something stronger?'

'Tea's fine for us, especially in your house,' replied Felicity. Kay led the way slowly into a large, bright sitting room, where a long picture window faced the spectacular view down the hill and across to the River Dee. She lowered herself into an old green Parker Knoll facing the window and indicated to us to make ourselves comfortable.

Although I hadn't visited Kay's house since boyhood, I felt at once that I was in familiar surroundings. There were several pictures of views I recognised, a large painting of the lake at Kandy, and several sepia photographs of the Ceylon Highlands. Under the window there was an old wooden Dutch-style octagonal storage box, sitting on square carved wooden elephant's feet and covered in brass fittings.

Kay was scanning through a pile of post that had been left by her chair. Her hair was black with a dramatic grey streak either side of a parting, and on the lapel of her jacket was a gold clip, studded with small white stones and with a large blue jewel in the centre. Felicity had noticed it too.

'Kay, may I ask, that's a wonderful piece on your lapel; what is it?'

Kay looked down at it, smiled and blinked as though fighting back a tear. 'It's pre-war,' she said eventually. 'White and blue sapphires, from Siedle, the best jeweller in Colombo. Com gave it to me when I was Audrie's bridesmaid.'

'Oh, how lovely, and so thoughtful to wear it today,' Felicity responded, 'what a wonderful idea.'

'What was life like there, before you were married?' I asked. 'You and Audrie were great friends.'

'Of course,' Kay laughed. 'Joined at the hip. In and out. I was eighteen in the year of the coronation, in the days when Com and Audrie had just met. Your grandfather, Finch, had been a friend of my Pa and when she first came back, she often stayed with us at Justice House. That's how we became such buddies. Coronation Week in Colombo was an enchanting round of celebrations. There were tennis tournaments, parades, swimming parties, and then cocktail parties, dinners, and fancy dress balls every night. And soon after, it was Rowing Week and then Cricket Week, all with their celebrations.'

I noticed that beside me, Felicity was equally fascinated. This, I reminded myself, was the carefree world my mother had lived in as a young woman, so how did that prepare her for life in post-war England, widowed, alone, with two young boys and everything rationed?

I moved to be nearer Kay's chair. 'Can I ask you something else, about Colombo, that's been intriguing me?'

'Of course, darling.'

'Who were Nellie and Bunny? Were they sisters? In Colombo?'

'Nellie and Bunny? Oh, I know what you mean, not sisters, they were husband and wife,' she laughed. 'Nelly was the man, Nelly short for Nelson, Bunny and Nelly Nelson. I've forgotten what his real name was. John. Why, have they reappeared?'

'Yes, in a way. I've been reading about them, in Com's letters.' I leaned forward, elbows on knees.

'What sort of letters?'

'Com's to her, hers to her people and so on. Hundreds of them.'

'I understand. Yes, she was a great hoarder,' Kay responded. 'Go on.'

I sat back. Felicity was looking across at the hills rising into the darkening sky.

'Even when she was giving away furniture left and right, she never let me throw out the letters,' I continued. 'She finally gave them to me before she moved to the care home. But when I asked her about Com on my last visit, she still wouldn't talk about him. She wanted me not to go over the letters until after she'd gone.'

'Did she never tell you about her life with Com? Or about Susan?' Kay frowned.

'No, she didn't,' I responded. 'And I didn't even know I had a sister until I saw Audrie's will last week. When was she born? Do you know what the story is, Kay?'

'Good God. She never told you about Susan? And what happened in South Africa?' Kay was wide-eyed, clearly shocked.

'No, never. And I still don't know,' I continued. 'Did you ever see Susan?'

'Yes, of course, I knew about her. I saw her probably once or twice.' Kay drew a deep breath and turned to face me. She spoke quietly and steadily. 'She was born in the summer of '41, before all the Japan chaos started. Com and Audrie were constantly worrying about Susan, that she wasn't putting on any weight. But when the Japs were expected to invade Ceylon as well, all the European families had to be evacuated. She went to South Africa, and took Robin and Susan with her. Poor little mite. I'm sure there will be lots about her in her letters. Do you know if she's still alive?'

'I've no idea. A week ago I'd never heard of her. There are dozens, probably hundreds, of letters sent to and from South Africa in that pile. I've started reading them, but so far only the early stuff from when they first met. Nothing about her. Do you think she might be?' Thoughts and ideas were tumbling through my head. If Susan was still in South Africa, why had Audrie never gone back there?

'We could go down there and try and find her. I mean, if she was born in 1941 she'd be in her fifties now.' I glanced at Felicity, who nodded back, supportive.

Kay shut her eyes as she returned to her memories. 'I do hope she is. She wasn't well from the first days. I remember the day Audrie told me she was pregnant, we were lunching at the GOH. We often used to meet there. It was a magical building on the corner by the port. There were tiled floors with rugs which Ticia used to slide about on.

The great dining room had a resident orchestra, and fans on long poles. Neil used to boast that he had swung on one in his wilder days. Then, after lunch, we'd go shopping, often starting at the Colombo Apothecaries, your father's firm, or Cargill's and then on into the Pettah.'

Kay lifted her cup and sipped her tea, as if she'd said enough.

'Sadly it's gone now,' I remembered, 'or we didn't see it when we were there. But d'you know why Com didn't, or couldn't, go with her? On the ship, I mean?'

'He wanted to, of course, darling,' Kay said,' but he was reserved. He was head of the biggest pharmaceutical firm, they needed him there to manage all the medical supplies.'

'But, were you there in Colombo when Com died?' I was nervous of what we might find out.

'No, darling,' Kay replied. 'Soon after Neil and I were married, we were posted up to Belgaum in India.' Kay's accent had never changed with the decades. She said *married*. 'All members of the CPRC were sent off in batches of thirty or so for officer training.'

'CPRC?' asked Felicity. 'Was that army?'

'Colombo Planters' Rifle Corps,' Kay explained. 'Volunteers, all European expatriates. But once the war started, pretty well compulsory for all the civilian men, not just the planters.'

'But Belgaum was a god-forsaken spot,' she went on, 'no telegrams, no post to speak of, so when Com died, we didn't hear until months later. Poor Audrie. God knows what she went through. It was hard for us all to keep in touch.'

'You didn't see her again, in Colombo?'

'No, darling, not until we came home in the early fifties. But we used to write. She was completely shattered when he died, such a tragedy, not just his death but whether…' she hesitated, …'if it could have been prevented.'

'What do you mean?'

'Darling, it was her story. She worried for years, she must have felt some sort of remorse, I don't know, but she should have told you, not me. But did you never ask her?'

'Several times, but it was no good.'

Kay nodded, as if not surprised.

'Of course. You never knew Com. He was such a character.' Smiling at the thought, Kay leaned back in her chair, and shut her eyes for a moment.

'Back then in Ceylon before the war, all the girls were a little in love with him. He seemed much more mature than all the other young men. He was wonderful company, to young or old, and you know he and Neil had been close friends since they shared in that chummery. It was through Com that I first met Neil in '37, about the time he and Audrie got engaged.'

'And he was an excellent bridge partner.' Kay turned to her daughter, who was pouring tea for everyone. 'Better than your father, Ticia dear, I'm sorry to say. They were great pals but none of us ever felt we knew him completely. He kept much to himself, perhaps from being Aberdonian.'

I felt as an orphan might do on discovering that he had parents after all. Why couldn't Audrie have ever told me stories like this? Now, on the day of her funeral, I felt even more frustrated at her lifetime of reticence.

'I think I've learned more about my father in these last three hours,' I said to Felicity as we checked in for the flight back to London, 'than in the whole of the rest of my life so far.'

'Of course, darling,' Felicity grinned. 'Kay was fascinating. Now you can go back to the letters. Maybe the answers will all be there.'

Over the next few weeks, most of my spare time was spent poring over the remaining boxes of letters and papers from Audrie's archive. In a letter she had written to her mother, I uncovered part of the mystery of my missing sister. She was in South Africa. Once I had the whole story, I could write it all down. I went back to the pile.

One envelope, among the hundreds, looked completely different. It was much more recent, a small sheet of old-fashioned cream laid paper, with a crest on the envelope which I recognised.

IMPERIAL WAR MUSEUM,

LAMBETH, LONDON SE

TEL: RELIANCE 8922

March 14th, 1960
Mrs. A.J Sutherland
Grace Cottage,
Piltdown,
Sussex

Dear Madam,

<u>The Wartime Notebooks of R.W. Sutherland, Esq.</u>

Thank you for your letter of March 3rd addressed to the
Library here, which has been passed to the archive section for
which I am responsible.

The offer of your late husband's wartime notebook is a most
generous gesture, which is much appreciated. I would be
delighted to have sight of it whenever it would be convenient.
We will then study it over a period of approximately one
month, and then let you have our decision.

Concerning delivery here, we would understand perfectly if
you do not wish to send the material by post, and if you would
prefer to bring them here in person, I should be happy to meet
you. Perhaps if you would care to telephone this office, we can
make the appropriate arrangements either way?

I remain, Madam,
Yours faithfully,

Harold Cordery

H.A. Cordery
Department of Documents

On the Imperial War Museum website, I researched the archives under his name, and there was a note with a keyword precis.

R.W. Sutherland: Diaries of civilian and business life in Colombo, 1942–45. Work at FECB Colombo; Experiences with Japanese war codes.

War Codes? FECB? I looked up the initials, and what I found opened a completely new window on my father's life.

The Far East Combined Bureau, (FECB), an outstation of the Government Code and Cypher School at Bletchley Park, was set up in in March 1935, to monitor Japanese intelligence and radio traffic. Later it moved to Singapore and then Colombo (Ceylon).

Did Audrie know about FECB, wherever that was? Why had she kept the War Museum's letter? I felt like a character in a thriller who, just as soon as he feels he's discovering the truth, finds he's been tricked all along. How many more layers of secrets had Audrie left behind? Did she want me to find these things, or had she just forgotten they were there?

Having made an appointment to view the diary, I took the underground to Lambeth North, and walked across the lawn, under the huge naval guns, to the museum. Inside, I zigzagged between the school parties gazing up at the V1 rocket, the Spitfire, at the tanks and guns and mortars, and climbed up the stairs at the back to the Reading Room. After filling in the usual forms for a reader's ticket, I found an empty desk, handed in the ticket to the librarian, and waited for my item to be found and brought out.

A few minutes later, a note was delivered to the desk, saying the item was ready for collection. At the counter a porter handed me a box folder, with the name R.W. Sutherland, and the file numbers typed in on the spine.

'Here we are, sir. Let my colleague on the desk know if you'd like to make any photocopies.'

I signed for it, half-expecting the porter to ask if there was any connection between my reader card and the name on the folder, but probably he didn't even look and certainly wasn't concerned. With some trepidation I undid the string holding the box door shut, and inside there it was. Even though I'd never heard of it a week before, and never seen it until that moment, the book inside felt instantly familiar. It wasn't a diary at all. It was a large brown and green notebook, with the logo of the Colombo Apothecaries Company on the cover. As soon as I opened it, I knew the search had been justified. There was the handwriting that I'd got to know in the past few weeks of transcribing the letters.

Cypher: a secret means of communication
Cypher Message: A message, the content of which consists entirely
of cypher groups
Procedure message: A message, the subject matter of which consists
of one or more procedure and/or operator signals together with any
groups or words amplifying signals

Com hadn't written daily entries, but a series of notes, some dated, others not. Clearly, the censor had prevented him from writing to Audrie about the war work he was doing. There was so much more to his life in Colombo than I, or even Audrie, until she'd read this – if she had – would have ever known about. His notes in the Apothecaries book revealed that he had, after all, been involved in the war – the secret war of Station X, Bletchley Park.

I had thought looking through a few pages would be enough. But the next thing I knew, I'd been reading for three hours, and the porter was tapping my shoulder.

'Six o'clock, sir, excuse me, closing, all items to be returned.'

I replaced the notebook in its box, handed it back in, and made an appointment to return a few days later.

As I travelled home, I wondered how this discovery would fit the story. Everything I'd read would have to be studied again, carefully, along with the rest of the letters. Another puzzle. Had Audrie ever read the notebook? Had she given it to the museum because of what it contained? When she had given the notebook to the museum, back in the early sixties, the Ultra code breaking story was still classified.

At home, I told Felicity what I'd discovered.

'I'll go through the rest of the letters and papers, try and find out about my Pa, and what happened to him and to Susan. And maybe discover why Audrie never spoke about any of it.'

'Do you even know how he died,' Felicity asked, 'or when?'

'Not sure. The gravestone in Colombo gave his date of death, June 16, 1946. I'll start from there.'

At the Colindale Newspaper library in north London, I searched the Ceylon newspaper archives for the editions on the dates near my father's death, and in *The Times of Ceylon* of 17 June 1946, there it was.

SNAKE BITE KILLS MR R.W. SUTHERLAND

Mr Sutherland, Managing Director of the Colombo Apothecaries Co, died yesterday as a result of being bitten by a snake while walking near Colombo Race Course. Mr Sutherland, who was also Managing Director of the Kandy Hotels Company, was in Ceylon for many years, and closely associated with sports and social activities. He was well known as a chess player. He had been waiting for a ship to take his family home to England, where he was to take charge of an important chemical concern. He leaves his wife, formerly Miss Finch Noyes, and two children. The funeral takes place at Kanatte General Cemetery at 5.30 pm today.

My father's life, in three paragraphs? So it had been a snake. What a terrible death. How awful for Audrie. I'd been less than a year old. I drove home wondering how it could have happened.

'Snakebite? How awful. I read about the risk of snakes in the Sri Lanka guidebook,' said Felicity, when she arrived an hour later. 'What does it mean? What can we do now?'

'I'll write it all down,' I decided, 'for Robin's boys and for their children. I don't like unfinished business.'

'Where will you start?'

'At the beginning.'

TWO

Indian Ocean, January 1937

An hour or so before dawn, the Orient Line's Royal Mail Steamer *Orontes* was making nineteen knots across the southern Indian Ocean, heading for the port of Colombo. Promptly at six o'clock, her master stepped onto the bridge and strolled over to the wheel, where the duty deck officer and the helmsman came to attention.

'Good morning, Mr Harris, QM.' Captain Baillie leaned forward to peer out at the night sea. 'Position? Course? Forecast?' Next to him, the young quartermaster clenched the wheel, and turned to his officer, who nodded. 'Go ahead, Bowers.'

'Good morning, Captain, sir,' the helmsman responded. 'Approximately twenty-five miles WNW of Colombo, steering one-o-four, sir. Set fair, slight breeze from the south, sir.'

'Bring her up a little, son,' Baillie encouraged, 'perhaps three points. We'll want to approach from the north. The tide will be running past the harbour entrance.'

'Steer one-o-one.' The officer of the watch reached forward to make a note in the log. 'Port three degrees it is, sir, steer one-o-one.'

Out in the fresh air, early risers strolled around the promenade decks, occasionally clutching a handrail as the ship's bow dipped and rose, elegant in the long ocean swells.

An hour later, Audrie Finch Noyes awoke to a tearing, grating noise which, to her unfocussed mind, sounded as though the ship had collided with something very hard. She slid out of her bunk, reached for her dressing gown, leaned over and pressed her nose to the porthole. It was dawn, not the slow budding dawn of her Sussex schooldays, but the flash of tropical transformation. 'We're only seven degrees from the equator,' her father used to say. 'No seasons here to speak of.'

Through the salt-crusted window she could see the shapes of the cranes and masts of Colombo harbour, and to the right, the long outline of the city, with its low palms along the front. Further along, there was the familiar shape of the Galle Face Hotel. She remembered the children's Christmas party, hating the frilly dress and wishing she could be with the grown-ups instead. Now that she was back, she'd be able to do exactly what she wanted.

The metal grinding stopped abruptly, and as the normal sounds gradually returned, she understood. It must have been the anchor dropping, while they waited for a ship to come out of the harbour. With her cheek still pressed against the glass, Audrie watched the scene change as *Orontes* began to swing slowly around to face south, away from the harbour entrance. As she turned back to her washstand, there were three soft knocks at the cabin door.

'What is it?' She dabbed her face with a towel.

'Florence, Miss Finch Noyes.' A muffled voice. 'Your tea, Miss. It's seven o'clock. We're just outside Colombo harbour.'

Audrie opened the door to the smiling cabin stewardess, who edged past her, balancing a loaded tray. 'Thank you, Flo. I heard the anchor being dropped. It startled me.'

'Good morning, Miss.' Florence, smart but matronly in her white uniform, was a familiar face for the Finch Noyes family, who'd always made a point of asking if she was available and of giving her a large tip at the beginning of each passage. Now, she bustled about, arranging the tea things on the low table beside the bunk.

'We're probably waiting for a ship to come off the Orient mooring. We'll be inside in an hour or so.' She poured tea. 'Did you sleep well, Miss Audrie? Happy to be back again?'

'I should say so. Good morning to you, Flo. We weren't too late. I had to dance with the same young man four times.' She picked up the jug and sniffed it. 'Is this fresh milk?'

'No, Miss, we finished the last crate two days ago. It's Carnation. And which young man would that be?'

'Carnation? Just as well we've arrived. Spoils good tea. I'll take it without.' Audrie picked up the cup and took a sip.

'You should know, dear, after all.' Tea trade families were regular passengers on the Orient Line.

'It was Michael de something,' Audrie added. 'Sweet boy, very young.'

The stewardess looked askance at her; Audrie couldn't be more than twenty-one. 'But look,' she said, picking up the blue silk dress Audrie had worn the previous evening, 'you are such an untidy girl, I must say, a lovely gown like that, tossed over a chair.' She folded it with great expertise, and laid it on Audrie's open suitcase.

'So sorry.' Audrie grimaced at her, then laughed. 'Thank you, dear Flo. You've looked after me so well. I do hope I get you on the return passage in six months' time. I promise to tell you all my adventures.'

'It'd be a pleasure to look after you again, Miss Audrie.' Flo gave her a motherly smile, as she opened the drawers of the fitted chest in the corner of the cabin, pulling out two silk slips Audrie had missed. She folded them and handed them to Audrie, who tucked them into the corner of her case.

'Thank you, well spotted. Is my aunt up yet? When do I need to be ready?' She sipped more tea. 'Not bad tea at last. Did you have a word with the stillroom steward? Small leaf, five minutes in the pot, no more?'

'Yes, Miss Audrie, I told him what you said. He's doing it properly now,' she confirmed. 'Mrs Mann asked to be called at six.' Florence picked up the hairbrush Audrie had dropped beside the dressing table. 'The agent's launch will be coming out soon now, and we'll be in harbour to start unloading cargo at about half past nine. And when you've finished packing, Miss Audrie, just leave everything by the door, I'll double-check before they take it down.'

'Thank you so much, Flo. You're an absolute poppet.' Audrie glanced across at the little green leather-bound travelling clock, beside the bunk, which her father had given her for her twenty-first birthday. She had reset it at Naples and again at Port Said and the hands were still at four-fifteen. It must be past midnight back home. She would need to change the time again.

'Will that be all, Miss Audrie?'

'Thank you, yes. Is the bathroom free?'

'It should be, Miss, just a sec.' Flo crossed the corridor and pushed open the door of the bathroom opposite. 'It's free.'

'Thank you. I'll see you before I go up.'

As the stewardess closed the cabin door, Audrie pulled out a ten-shilling note from her purse and placed it under her water glass. She opened the door, checked the corridor left and right, and stepped quickly across into the bathroom. As she undressed she paused for a moment to look at herself in the mirror on the back of the door. Her blue eyes looked back at her strong cheekbones and her new bob. Perhaps she'd lost a little weight on the voyage? She stuck her tongue out at her image, tucked her hair into the bath cap, and stepped into the shower.

Below in the swirling, greasy water of Colombo harbour, the Orient Line's launch tied up alongside *Orontes*. Port officials and medical officers jumped from their tender alongside, and climbed up to start their inspection.

———————

Outside on the promenade deck, Peggy Mann leaned with her elbows on the rail, watching the busy tug's foaming wake as it nudged *Orontes'* bow past the end of the mole and into the inner harbour.

Now that *Orontes* was closer to the land, Peggy detected the familiar scents that had begun to waft across the water, combining the rich, dark fragrances of jasmine and spices with the more earthy aromas of sewerage, drains and rotting vegetation.

It was always the wives who suffered most with the travelling. This was Peggy's fifth return trip in ten years, back and forth to be with the children for the school summer holidays. They had left London early in the New Year, and the three-week voyage was one of the few treats she enjoyed, although she couldn't ever decide whether she preferred going out or coming home. It was hateful taking the children back to school, poor little tykes, starting boarding when they were only seven or eight. But coming out this time had been made much more fun having Audrie along.

Every five years when Ham got leave, they'd take a house in Sussex for six months, and then she would have to start all over again. Now she'd been to-ing and fro-ing like this since their elder child had first come home to start school years before.

Peggy often compared her life in Ceylon with that of her sister who, since she married, had hardly ever left Hampshire. True, Peggy and Ham did enjoy their expatriate lives, the warmth, the servants, the social life and clubs, but they had paid a price in the hardships of primitive up-country life on a tea estate, and in not seeing their children grow up. Peggy's two teenage boys had already sailed across the world, and knew their way around two cultures, while her sister's children had probably never been more than ten miles from their mother. While Peggy ran the estate bungalow and worried about their little family, Ham was out working all day, dawn to dusk, obsessed as much with the health and wellbeing of their two hundred pickers and staff at the estate as he was with the quality of their tea. By contrast, her sister and brother-in-law's life at home, when she had stayed with them last month, seemed so dull and colourless. Would she swap her life with Angela's? Never.

Now, she hoped there would be just one more year until he retired and then they'd be home, thank God, and that would be it. That was a point. Ham retired would be a menace around the house. She'd have to work out how to keep him from under her feet.

'Glad to be back, Auntie Peg?' Audrie's voice lifted her out of her reverie. Audrie, now in a fitted white linen dress printed with large black flowers, and a small white hat on the back of her head, put a hand on the rail beside her, and shaded her eyes. It had been so nice for Peggy to have her god-daughter on passage with her. She was such great company, and her lively personality and constant chatter had helped Peggy get over her usual depression when parting from her children.

'Only eight o'clock and it's pretty hot already. Can you see him?'

'Not yet,' Peggy replied. 'But he'll be down there somewhere waving his spotted hanky. He's always early. Oh, that dress looks wonderful, Audrie darling, very cool and elegant. You'll give the young men a great deal to think about. Talking of young men, who was the fellow last night in the smoking room? He seemed very interested.'

Audrie smoothed the material across her waist. 'Do you like it? From Marshalls. Mums helped me choose it. He's Michael de something. I danced with him after you went to bed. It's his first trip. He's come out to start as creeper. His tropical kit's all new. I don't think he's got the foggiest what to expect.'

She leaned on the rail to watch the tenders loading below. Two coolies let a large crate slip onto the deck, the supervisor started to swear at them, but was quickly shushed by the officer.

'Don't be beastly to him, poor boy,' responded her godmother, patiently. 'He's probably very shy. Your father was the same one day. And when Ham and I met, he'd been here for five years and except for his superintendent's wife, he hadn't spoken to a white woman for six months.' She opened her bag to dig out a fan and unfolded it.

'Six months? How perfectly ghastly.' Audrie turned to watch the unloading on the landing stage. 'But I wasn't beastly to him. In fact I was quite charming. He's been learning bridge. He wants me, I mean us, to join his party after dinner at the Galle Face tomorrow. Today, rather.' Below her, she could see half a dozen porters in white cotton shirts, now loading suitcases, trunks and boxes onto the tenders which had tied up alongside.

'I thought he'd taken a fancy,' Peggy laughed. 'And why not? He'll be off up-country in a day or so and won't have a decent social life for quite a while. And yes,' she continued, 'I expect we'll dine at the Galle Face. Or at the Garden Club. We usually do, first night back. Ham loves a bit of company and a good chinwag with his chums when he gets down to Colombo.'

Below them, the agent clattered back down the port side gangway to the waiting launch, his crew performing immaculate naval drill with the boat hooks, before it sped back to the dockside.

'Yes, Audrie, I do love coming back,' Peggy said. 'Even after so many trips, it's still one of the most exciting moments, arriving on a big ship.' She paused. 'Coming or going, it's always the end of one episode and the start of another one. An old chapter closes, another begins. *Landfall and departure mark the rhythmical swing of a seaman's life and a ship's career.*' She turned towards her niece with a smile. 'From Conrad's *Mirror of the Sea*. I was having dinner at the Captain's table, on passage out years ago, and he declared that this line described his life perfectly. I've always thought it was the same for us out here, opening and closing a chapter with every passage out or home.'

'Well, I hope it's an exciting new chapter for me,' Audrie sighed. 'A whole new book would be nice. I'm so glad I got away from London after that beastly Edward episode.'

'So is everyone, darling.'

The young man Audrie had met the evening before appeared on the rail nearby. He must have been about the same age as her, Peggy guessed, but how young he looked, in his brand-new tropical suit. Feeling rather sorry for him, Peggy nudged Audrie and nodded in his direction. Audrie turned, smiled and walked over. 'Good morning, Michael, how are you today?'

'Much better, thank you, Miss Finch Noyes.'

'Audrie. Please call me Audrie.' They gazed at the view along the harbour. 'My aunt says if your people are going, we'll see you after dinner at the Galle Face Hotel.'

The young man beamed at her. 'Golly, how wonderful. But where exactly is it? I mean, is it far? I'm being met by my boss and staying at a hotel in Fort, and we're going up to the country in a couple of days.'

'It's "up-country",' she smiled, aware that she probably sounded patronising. 'We say "up-country". Just about everywhere except the coast is "up". This is Fort, here in front of us. You're probably staying at the Bristol or the Grand Oriental. Most passengers stop there the night they arrive or before they leave.'

'Is Fort a real Fort?' Michael turned towards her.

'Mostly shops and offices now,' Audrie explained. 'My father's office used to be just up the road there. The original Dutch fort had proper walls and a moat and guns. But they've all gone now. And opposite the landing stage, that's the old GOH, the Grand Oriental, with the columns, see? Down there, that long green park, with the palms, along by the beach, that's Galle Face Green where they all play cricket, and at the end, the hotel. They have a dinner dance several nights a week. The food's always the same.' Audrie knew she was merely repeating her mother's mantra, as she had never been to even one Galle Face dinner dance. She'd taken passage home with her mother to start school, when she was just eight. But she'd heard so many wonderful stories about the frolics and parties from Peggy and her mother that she felt she'd been there several times.

Below them, there was a huge crash as a crate being lowered by the ship's crane landed heavily on a tender alongside. They stared down as it was lifted and repositioned.

'Righto, thank you awfully much. I do hope to see you there.' The young man stepped back, shook hands rather sheepishly and bounded off to fetch his things; Audrie watched him leap down the tweendeck companionway. She still couldn't remember his surname.

'There he is,' Peggy pointed. 'There's Ham, waving his hanky. He always has his big hanky.'

A hundred yards away, between the tall white pillars at the end of the covered landing quay, a plump man in a white suit and solar topee was waving a large blue spotted handkerchief, as he scanned the length of the ship. Audrie leaned forward over the rail, stuck two fingers in her mouth, gave an ear-splitting whistle, and then waved. Ham immediately turned, paused for a few seconds till he found them, and then started to wave back furiously, at the same time pointing to the quayside exit.

'Darling, I'm shocked.' Peggy turned to her, mouth wide open. 'Most unladylike. But impressive. I've never heard anything like it, not from a girl. For pity's sake don't do it again or Ham will make the most frightful fuss. Where on earth did you learn to do that?'

'The doorman at Arden showed me. He was adorable.' She put up her hand as a gust of warm wind caught her hat. 'He used to make huge tips, whistling up cabs for clients in Bond Street. Shall we go down and see where they've got our cases?'

As they stood in the queue for the launch, an assistant purser offered Audrie a leaflet. 'Good morning, Miss, the Orient Line Guide to Colombo. Helpful information for your visit. Make the most of your stay.'

'Thank you, Gilbert, good morning.' Audrie smiled at him. 'But not necessary.' As the leading tender launch touched the foot of the first class gangway, two sailors reached for the painters and made them fast. The boatman expertly held his craft alongside the ship, while the first group stepped down, each woman handed into the boat by a crew member, all the while deep in conversation. Its complement of passengers safely seated, the tender sped the hundred yards across the inner harbour to the shaded Passenger Pier, where Ham and several dozen others stood expectantly. Audrie and Peggy waited their turn, and finally stepped up onto the quay.

Ignoring the tumult around them, Peggy and Ham hugged and kissed each other, in the tender way of people used to long separations. Remembering her own parents' similar meetings and farewells, either painful or joyous but nearly always tearful, Audrie stood a little way from them, watching the scene along the landing quay. A dozen other families greeted their own returning members; tanned Europeans in shorts or white suits shook hands with returning old colleagues or paler new arrivals.

Disentangling himself eventually from his wife, Ham kissed Audrie and stepped back, holding her shoulders while he looked at her.

'How are you, Audrie dear? I must say you do look very lovely.'

'Dear Uncle Ham, I'm so hap…' Before she could say more, he took both women's arms. 'Come on,' he urged, 'tell me all the news while we wait for the bags to come off.' Once at the gate, Ham turned to collar one of the many shipping agent's checkers, and became his usual efficient self, giving orders, bustling about, calling out to the porters as they struggled to bring luggage ashore from the service tenders.

'Peg, where's your luggage list? Are Audrie's on the same one? How many pieces? Darling, which of the trunks did you bring? Are there any more to come up from Not Wanted?'

Having silenced her usual chatter to greet her husband, Peggy now began to return to normal as they waited for their cases and trunks to be delivered to the waiting car.

'Ham darling, tell me, how are your knees? Any more malaria attacks? Have you been taking your pills? Is all well at Glenugie?' They stood for fifteen minutes exchanging all their news, until two huge carts, towed by vast white oxen, and laden with luggage, lumbered down the quayside towards them and the crowd pushed back to let them pass.

Another motor launch drew alongside and Audrie saw the young Englishman from the ship jump ashore, carrying a large suitcase, to be greeted by a very tall, sandy-haired man in a solar topee, khaki shirt and shorts. As he and the youngster emerged into the sun and approached the baggage collection area, he spotted the Manns, strode up to them, placed himself firmly between them and put his arms round their shoulders.

'Ham, old man. Peg, how lovely to see you,' he exclaimed. 'Just back? How was the passage?'

'Better than most, Charlie dear,' responded Peggy, and turned to Audrie. 'I had my god-daughter, Audrie Finch Noyes, with me.'

'Audrie,' interrupted Ham, taking her arm, 'may I present Charles Burrows, one of our most respected planters. He was a great friend of your Pa, in spite of the fact that he's not only Scottish but works for the competitor. Charlie, Miss Audrie Finch Noyes.'

They shook hands. 'How d'ye do. But, Audrie, of course, of course we met when you were a little girl and I'd just come out. How lovely you look. Fresh as a daisy, while we're all a wee bit sticky from waiting in the sun.' As if to illustrate his point, he pulled out a huge handkerchief from his trouser pocket, took off his topee and wiped his brow. 'We all miss your father. How's he getting on?'

They stood back for a moment as a porter laden with three huge cases struggled past them towards a car.

'He's fine, or at least he was in January,' Audrie replied, looking up at him. 'Going up to town every day. But he misses life out here.'

'Excellent show. Can't keep a good man quiet. Give him my best when you write.' Burrows placed his hand on Michael's shoulder and introduced his companion. 'This laddie is my new assistant, Michael de St Aubin. Michael, meet Mr and Mrs Mann, and their niece, Audrie Finch Noyes.'

'How do you do, sir. Hello again, Mrs Mann, how d'you do.'

'We met on the boat,' Audrie interrupted. De St Aubin. No wonder she hadn't remembered. 'Perhaps we'll see you at the Galle Face.'

'Will you definitely be there? Are you staying in town?' Michael was still gazing at Audrie, his hair flopping over his forehead and his eyes wide in his large, freckled open face.

'We'll be at the company bungalow down in Colpetty for a couple of days before we go up-country,' Ham announced. 'Tonight's the usual Thursday dinner jamboree, so we'll come on there after the Garden.'

'Everyone drops in on their first evening,' Audrie explained to Michael. 'So the whole town soon knows you're back in Colombo.'

As the porters deposited the last two trunks next to them, the gleaming black company Humber crept slowly forward and stopped. The driver, immaculate in his white tunic and trousers, leaped out and saluted Peggy and Audrie.

'Welcome home, Lady. Welcome, Missy.'

'Hello, Wimal, it's good to be back,' Peggy said warmly. 'How have you been?'

'Most well, thank you, Lady.' He opened the door for them and went round to supervise the luggage with Ham. Cases were loaded into the boot and the biggest trunk strapped to the back of the car. A second van drew up for their remaining pieces.

'Make sure they deliver the big trunk straight home,' Peggy wagged a finger at the driver.

Wimal nodded side to side, Ceylon fashion. 'Of course, Lady, straight to Bungalow.'

Audrie gave her small valise and her beauty box to the driver, and turned to the others. 'After dinner, then?'

'By all means. Goodbye for now.' Burrows and his new assistant set off towards a parked estate van.

Audrie, Ham and Peggy climbed into the car and sat back. Peggy thrust an arm into the bottom of her large bag, looking for her fan. They waved to the two men as the motor edged forward through the throng, towards the Harbour Gate and out into the streets of Colombo Fort.

'What do you think?' Ham announced to nobody in particular. 'A few days in town, and then back up to Maskeliya? Glad to be back? What have you been up to at home?'

'Glad? You bet,' said Audrie, twisting in her seat to watch three small boys playing cricket in the road. 'What've I been up to? Didn't Aunt Peggy tell you about my disastrous romance?'

Ham turned to her, raising an eyebrow. 'No, do tell.'

'Beastly Edward Elliot.' She gave him a bright smile. 'He proposed, I accepted, we announced the engagement and then he dumped me. Horrible man.'

Sussex, England, 1936

Audrie had first floated the idea of leaving home a few months before her twenty-first birthday. It was just a year since her parents had retired from Ceylon and returned to England, for Finch to continue his career at the tea company's head office in London.

The family were in the dining room at Coldblow, their rented house in Sussex, with its pink wallpaper and dark mahogany sideboards. Audrie and her sister Chim never felt comfortable there and when her parents were out, they much preferred to have lunch in the kitchen with Mrs Page.

'Dads, are you going up to London tomorrow? Can I have a lift into Haywards Heath?' She picked up an apple from a Kandy silver fruit bowl on the table and examined it for bruises. Her father, finishing the last mouthful of his grilled sole, nodded, and wiped his grey moustache with his napkin.

'Why, darling? Do you want to go shopping?' He lifted the

watch from the pocket of his waistcoat and held it up.

'Not shopping, I can't afford anything.' She bit into the apple. 'No, to tell the truth I'm going up to see an employment agency to get a job. I'm bored stiff stuck here in the country, and I want to do something, earn some money.' She finished the apple and started picking at a bunch of grapes.

'What?' He turned to Audrie's mother. 'Do you know anything about this?' Behind him, the grandfather clock chimed the hour.

'Not in the least,' said her mother. 'Don't pick, darling. Cut off a bunch and put it on your plate, that's what the scissors are for. What type of job, Audrie darling?'

'Not sure. Anything that suits. I thought a salon.' She picked up the pair of silver fruit scissors and cut off a handful.

'A salon? God's teeth! What's a salon?' Her father bristled. 'Those Chelsea artists?'

'A beauty salon, Finch dear,' said her mother. 'But, darling, surely you're not planning to be a hairdresser?'

'No, Mums, it's not that.' Audrie leaned towards her mother and lowered her voice. 'Julia Langton says in the place where she works, Arden in Bond Street, it's the most fashionable new beauty salon, they're looking for another girl to greet the clients, look after the reservations, answer the telephone. It'd be frightfully good experience. They have all sorts of smart clients.'

'Julia? The one you were at school with? Smart clients? In a salon?' said her mother. 'And what would your Aunt Clemency say if she walked in to have her hair done and there was her own niece working in a salon?'

'So what?'

'It would be very embarrassing, don't you understand?'

'Don't say "so what", Audrie,' her father's face reddened. 'It's American and very rude. Audrie, listen, let me be absolutely clear on this, I am not going to allow...'

'Oh, Dads, don't start all that "No daughter of mine" business, that went out twenty years ago in the war. Lots of girls have careers these days.'

'Well, a salon's not exactly a career, is it?' her mother interrupted.

'It could be. It's not as though Miss Randall's College qualifies you for office work. I've got to start somewhere. Julia says a trained beautician earns around twelve pounds a week – up to twenty with tips and commission. If I did well, I'd be promoted. Managers get much more. Even a girl working at a beauty counter in a store like Swan & Edgar makes between nine and twelve pounds a week. And if you're any good you make commission on top.'

'You don't have to start anywhere at all,' her father insisted again. 'You can stay right here. And I tell you, you will stay here. There's plenty to do in the country. The Newick Tennis Club, riding at Miss Longstaff's, golf here, the Dramatic Society, bridge. And I was planning to increase your allowance when you're twenty-one.'

'Bridge?' Audrie stood up from the table, drew a deep breath and put her hands on the back of her chair. 'Please excuse me, Mother and Father. You can stop me now, of course you can, but I'm going to be twenty-one soon and then you won't be able to stop me. I am not going to sit in the country and play bridge. I'm going to get a job in London. Julia says she's sure I could PG with her people.'

John Arthur Finch Noyes's mouth fell open, and he turned to his wife, who by this time was smiling. 'Paying Guest? Joy, where in heaven's name does she get these ideas? And why didn't she say before? And why are you grinning like an idiot?'

'She's a determined girl.' Audrie's mother dropped her napkin beside her plate, and rang the bell for Mrs Page. 'She gets that from you, Finch darling. I tried to ask her the other day what plans she had made, if any. She just looked at me and refused to discuss it. Just like you when you're plotting something.'

Finch allowed himself to grin. 'Bah to that. Do we even know the Langtons? Will she be safe with them? Didn't you say he was a rubber planter? Wouldn't trust them to sharpen a mamoty. I suppose it'll be all right.' As their housekeeper came in from the kitchen, he rose from the table and grumped his way out of the dining room.

Later that afternoon, Audrie wrote to her old school friend Julia in London. Yes of course, came the reply three days later, Mrs

Langton would be very happy to have her to stay at their house in South Kensington while Audrie started job-hunting, and once she started earning, she could pay two pounds a week towards her keep.

A week later, Audrie caught the train from Haywards Heath and took a bus from Victoria to the Langtons' house off the Old Brompton Road. The next day, when Julia introduced her to the manager of the Elizabeth Arden salon in Bond Street, Audrie's elegant looks and manner ensured her an offer. Within a few days, Audrie, wearing the chic Arden uniform, was making appointments, welcoming and settling customers, and watching how Miss Arden's beauticians earned their money.

At the end of the first week, she asked Julia's mother if she might use the telephone to call her parents.

'Mums. Guess what I'm holding! My first wage packet!'

Eventually, Joy and Finch, their anxiety suppressed by the knowledge that Audrie would be staying as a paying guest with Julia's family, reluctantly agreed to support the move. In the event, it brought Audrie not only her first salary, but her first, disastrous love affair.

Coldblow, Balcombe Road, Haywards Heath, 13th October

Darling Audrie

Thank you for the surprise telephone call, and I'm so, so sorry to hear the news, you poor lamb. Why didn't you say before? What a horrid man Edward turned out to be. I hope you are with Julia and her mother who, I am sure, will be a huge comfort to you and help you forget about all this.

Try and keep busy, concentrate on your work, and for the Lord's sake don't just sit around at the Langtons' and mope. This sort of thing happens to lots of people, and you mustn't be ashamed, you did absolutely the right thing to refuse to see him again, and darling I'm − we are both − very proud of you for how well you've behaved in all this.

Dads and I had a talk last night, and he's had an idea which might help you forget all this tumult of the last few months.

Would you like to go back to Ceylon for a break? Peggy Mann
has been home on leave for their children's holidays. It's her last
trip before Ham retires. She's sailing back to Colombo in the
New Year, and we thought it'd be a splendid idea if you could
travel out with her, and stay with them up at our old bungalow
at Glenugie for a few months, perhaps also with the Berrys
at Justice House, and come back in July. How would that suit
you? I'm not sure how much money you've saved at Arden,
but your Pa said he'd stand you the return passage, and of
course I could help you with some spending money. What
do you think?
We are looking forward to seeing you on Saturday for
your birthday – it will cheer us all up. I will pick you up
at Haywards Heath, telephone and let us know which train
you're taking.

Chin up.
Your loving
Mums

The large, faded sepia photograph was quite different from the
wedding portrait which had always lain on Audrie's dressing table.
It had been taken in Com's office, where the walls were plastered white
and the floors parquet-covered, and two lumbering fans continuously
fluttered the papers on the desk. There were wooden shutters on each
window, giving onto a little balcony overlooking the street below.
A calendar hanging on the office wall behind the subject showed
it had been taken in March 1929. Com would have been twenty-six,
newly arrived from Calcutta. Maybe, I pondered, the photograph
marked his arrival as the new manager of the Colombo branch? Or was
it for him to send home to his people?

Taken from across the room, perhaps by a professional, the
picture was more revealing of character than any I had seen.

In a white shirt, plain dark tie, and white suit trousers – in that heat the jacket would be hanging up somewhere – my father was leaning back in a wooden armchair with a pen in one hand, as though tapping it on the knuckles of the other. On the desk, a metal telephone handset rested on its cradle, two rush baskets held correspondence, while large paperweights secured piles of documents against the draught of the overhead fans. He held his chin down, looking firmly ahead at the far wall, ignoring the camera. His unruly curly hair was firmly brushed back with a suggestion of a side parting, and the photograph showed his full, wide mouth, with good, even teeth, dark, deep-set eyes, and the same prominent, straight nose that both of us had inherited.

Do I look like him? I wondered. And was he in that office the day he met my mother?

———————————

Robert 'Comrade' Sutherland was sitting at his desk, in the Cutler, Palmer office, when his assistant knocked on the office door. 'Mr Sutherland? Mr Bentley from the Galle Face returning your call.' Com nodded. A moment later the device rang, and he picked up the receiver.

'Com, dear boy. You called, how are you?' Michael was the perfect hotel manager; always immaculate, slightly camp, charming and efficient, fanatic about service.

'Michael, how are you? Can you hear me? Yes, I'm fine.' Com held the telephone receiver a few inches from his ear. 'Thanks for getting back to me. I'll tell you why I'm calling. Have you thought about early orders for the Coronation Balls? How many events are you putting on?… Delighted to hear it.' Through the frosted interior glass wall of his office, Com saw the silhouettes of his two managers, one six foot four and the other, five five, coming along the corridor for their usual Tuesday morning meeting.

As they appeared in the open doorway, he waved them to come in while he scribbled the hotel's orders on the pad on his desk. They each took a chair at the round table in the corner of the office.

The senior of the two, David Peacock, sales manager for Colombo, reached across to switch on a table fan, and Alan Druitt, for Hatton, Kelani Valley and Kandy, poured them each a glass from the bottle of Apollinaris water which sat on the table. The wooden shutters on the windows behind them were half-closed against the sun.

'Yes, I've got it, Michael. Thank you,' Com replied, leaning back in the chair. 'We'll messenger you the pro forma. Yes, it's all in stock. We ordered extra when the old king died, but then of course the Prince of Wales cancelled, as you might say. Our delivery boys will have them to you later this week. Need any more accessories? Soda, Tonic, Apollinaris? Ginger Beer? Angostura? Yes. Thank you. Fine, Michael, I'll be by this evening after dinner and maybe see you then. Goodbye.'

He replaced the receiver and turned his chair towards his colleagues, who were studying their sheets of sales figures.

'Good morning, Mr Sutherland. Sounds like a big order?'

'Morning, Alan, David. Michael Bentley at the Galle Face. A nice commission for you, David. He's pleased with the service since we took over from Mackenzie's. If we play it straight he'll help us get all the Schweppes business for Ceylon. The Galle Face are planning their Coronation Ball, in fact three Coronation Balls. But anyway, to Tuesday business.'

He wheeled his chair over to the side table, where a large cardboard box, covered with Indian postage stamps, lay with its top open. Com reached in and pulled out a pile of leaflets, and handed them to his colleagues.

'Take a look at what our blessed leaders have sent from above.'

'*The Book of Cutler Cups and Cocktails*,' said Peacock, turning it over in his hand. 'Is this from Bombay? My Lord, what are they thinking of now?'

'Head Office have sent us a thousand,' Com explained. 'Everyone's drinking cocktails again. Or maybe it's everyone in Bombay. Thought that had gone out with the twenties. Must be the new Duchess of Windsor. Apparently she likes daiquiris.' He got up from behind his desk and joined them at the table. 'God knows what we're expected to do with them all.'

Alan Druitt was browsing through the booklet. 'D'you fancy a *Glad Eye*? Or a *Bosom Caresser*? Perhaps we should give a party and test out a few of their recipes?'

'Don't be silly,' Com said. 'They give them such stupid names. God knows where they get them. It'll just be another fad. Give me a whisky and soda any day. Bombay want us to give them out to our customers. How many have we?'

'How many are there in Ceylon?' Peacock looked in his order book. 'Well, thinking of all the Colombo clubs and hotels, probably twenty-five. We could give them twenty copies each.'

'And up-country, Alan?' Com asked, tapping his pencil on the edge of the desk.

'Maybe twenty, and then of course all the district sports clubs,' Druitt calculated. 'More down south around Galle. Maybe a hundred in all. Five each would do fine.'

'Let's do that then, send them out with the monthly statements, or even better, you can hand them out personally when you make calls. What shall we do with the rest?'

'What about Mr Bentley at the Galle Face?' Peacock suggested. 'They're probably our biggest customer. A present to thank them for the big order. Certainly they'd go down well with the regulars before the Thursday dinner and dance. They could put them out on the little tables in the Veranda bar.'

'Good idea. I'm going down there tonight, some friends recently back from leave. I'll take these with me,' Com replied.

That evening, Com dined early at Sefton, the bachelor quarters which he shared with Neil Garland and Wilfred Amhurst, before driving down to the Galle Face Hotel. Switching off the motor, he could hear the waves of the Indian Ocean crashing onto the beach sixty yards away. There were groups of Sinhala families enjoying the warm evening air on Galle Face Green.

He sauntered through the double doors into the hotel lobby. He'd drop off the leaflets, see old Bentley again, pop in to the dining room, but he needed an early night. Two tall European girls in evening dress clacked arm in arm across the marble lobby, their heads close together, exchanging confidences. As they passed under the huge fan rotating slowly in the centre, its breeze caught them and they both raised a hand to hold their hair in place. Com watched them vanish through the ballroom doors before he approached the desk.

'*Ayubowan*, good evening, Mr Sutherland.' The head receptionist hurried over to greet him, joining his hands below his chin in the familiar Sinhala greeting.

'Good evening, Sunil. Is Mr Bentley about?'

'Not here at the moment, sir, but he's somewhere in the hotel. Shall I have a boy find him for you?'

'No need, another time.' Com handed over the packet. 'Can I leave this for him? Has Mr Nelson come out?'

'I believe they are still at their table, sir. May I show you the way?' He escorted Com across the lobby to the ballroom entrance and pushed open one of the large doors. The warmth and the noise of two hundred diners carrying on one hundred conversations hit Com like a wave.

'Thank you, Sunil. Don't worry, I can find them.'

As Com worked his way between the tables, dozens of white-coated waiters and assistants sped to and fro between the laughing and chattering guests, bearing drinks and food orders for latecomers. Several friends and acquaintances waved to him or stood up, inviting Com to join them; between the door and the corner, he stopped three times to shake hands and exchange news before finally arriving to join the Nelsons. His friend's party occupied a large table in the corner, including two other couples, and a good-looking woman he thought he recognised.

'Nelly, old bean, good to see you back,' said Com. 'How was the leave? Are you well? How was the passage out, any excitement?'

'None to speak of,' laughed John Nelson, standing to greet him. 'We got back two weeks ago. It was good to have a rest. These two were reasonably well behaved.' Com shook his friend's hand warmly and wrapped an arm round John's shoulder before moving round to kiss Bunny Nelson. The two other men stood up to shake his hand while their wives beamed up at him. Nelson made the introductions.

'Bernard and Marian Goff, Frank and Dorothy Henstock.'

'How d'ye do?' Com worked his way around the table, shaking hands. But then he stopped in front of the other guest, a very attractive woman in her late twenties, in a gold evening blouse, with a long, striking pale face, dark hair and, from what he could see, a beautiful figure.

'Com, this is Anna Maertens,' Bunny interrupted. 'I think you know – or knew – each other. She's back here for a month or two. She has people here, perhaps you know them?'

Com stared at her, at first unsure where they'd met. Then it came to him.

'Anna Maertens. Of course. Up at Nuwara Eliya,' he murmured, conscious that not only were the others watching them, but that they were the only single people in the group.

'Nuwara Eliya, that was it. I was staying with my uncle and aunt,' said Anna, smiling intently up at him and offering her hand. She touched and twisted the necklace which glittered at her throat. 'How charming of you to remember. I seem to recall we danced.' She paused, and then added: 'Several times.' Her hair fell across her face and she brushed it aside with a manicured hand.

'At the Grand Hotel,' said Com, not sure where this was leading, and if it did, what he wanted to do about it.

'Shall we sit?'

Com signalled a passing waiter who swiftly placed an extra chair next to Anna, while John cheerfully passed a bottle of what Com recognised as one of his firm's own Bordeaux reds.

'A whisky, Com, or would you care for a glass of claret?'

'The claret, thank you. You can trust this one to travel well. Welcome back,' he raised his glass to the rest of the table. 'Chin-chin.' He turned to the girl, who was still staring at him.

'So, Miss Maertens, how long are you staying here?'

'It's Anna. And it depends.' She raised an eyebrow.

'Anna,' he responded and pointed to his own chest. 'Robert. Or Com. On what?'

'Amongst other things,' she paused, taking a sip of wine, 'it could depend on you. Bunny and John thought you might like to show me the town. Are you still playing much golf?'

'As a matter of fact, I played this week,' said Com, 'but I murdered a chicken.' Anna giggled and their neighbours turned to listen to him.

'You what?' laughed John. 'A chicken?'

Com turned from Anna to look around the table. 'Yes, believe it or not. I had the distinction of slaying a hen on the golf course.'

'With an iron or a wood?' John grinned at him.

In for a penny, Com thought. 'A wood, a brassie, in fact. It was a nice full shot, good follow through, cleverly played with one eye on the ball and the other on the hen. It caught her slap behind the ear at a range of nine yards. Instantaneous slaughter.'

John let out a loud cackle. 'What? You must be pulling...'

'Unfortunately I was advised to stump up two rupees for the cost of the hen, and since my caddie belongs to some peculiar religion which doesn't allow him to carry hens as well as clubs, the achievement, albeit brilliant, must be considered as unproductive.'

'How sad for you.' Anna kept a straight face. 'And the hen? What did you do with it?'

'So,' he went on, 'but for this country's religious beliefs, I could have taken it home and proudly shown it to all my chums, but all I can do now is to show them – and you if you like – the brassie which killed it, and the notch in the handle thereof.'

Now they were all listening and John leaned across the table, beaming. 'What happened next? Did you win the hole?'

'The incident occurred at the long fourteenth. The hole is four hundred and seventy-five yards, par five,' Com continued in his best Bertie Wooster, 'and is the more remarkable for the fact that notwithstanding the loss of distance caused by the interruption of the ball's flight, I was down in five, to which the president of the club is willing to testify.'

'In five? How'd you do that?'

'To be precise, my hole was made up as follows.' He looked round the table. 'Drive, two hundred and fifty yards. Brassie shot to live hen, nine yards. Brassie shot from dead hen to green, two hundred and sixteen yards. Henry Cotton, writing in the *Sporting and*

Dramatic, will certainly describe the incident as an exceptionally fine shot for an amateur, requiring greater accuracy and judgement, as the slightest slice would probably have disturbed the hen's tail feathers, and possibly made egg laying uncomfortable for a few days.'

The party broke into laughter again, until Bunny touched her husband's elbow. 'Look who's blown in… Isn't that the Manns?' She turned to Bernard Goff. 'Wasn't she on passage down? And the girl?'

Goff peered across at the group moving between the tables towards them. 'Yes, I remember them. Of course. Peggy Mann, and Ham must've come down to meet them. Isn't he Eastern Produce? And yes, the girl was with her. Stunning looking.'

Com stared at the tall young woman who was walking towards their table with her older companions, and suddenly felt a little embarrassed by the girl sitting so close to his side. He couldn't help thinking – the newcomer was indeed stunning. She wore a dark blue silk dress which caught the glow of the thousand candles on the dining tables around the room. Her pale skin contrasted with her dark hair, which was cut short, with a fringe, in a style he hadn't seen before, showing off her high cheekbones. Com glanced sideways at Anna, who was pretending to study her menu. Her blouse suddenly looked very old-fashioned. He stood up to greet the newcomers.

'Gracious… I know exactly who that is,' said John, rising from his chair. 'It's the Finch Noyes's older girl, Audrie. He wrote to say Peggy was bringing her out and would we look out for her.' He took a couple of paces towards the new group, shook both Ham's and Peggy's hands, and greeted Audrie, turning and putting his hands on her and Peggy's shoulders as he guided them back to the table.

'Welcome back, Peggy,' John said to her and the table in general. 'For anyone in Ceylon who doesn't already know them, this is Ham and Peggy Mann, and may I introduce Miss Audrie Finch Noyes, whom I am sure everyone will want to know.' Ham and Peggy started greeting their old friends, and everyone else looked at Audrie.

'Good evening, everyone. It's lovely to be back.' Audrie gazed round the table as she spoke.

'Of course you'll join us?' John asked.

There was a general agreement, a shuffling of chairs and moving of glasses and a few seconds' confusion. Com circled the table to welcome Ham and Peggy and then, without really knowing how, found himself in front of Audrie. She looked at him for what seemed a long second, and then they shook hands.

'How d'ye do, Miss Finch Noyes.' She certainly looked spectacular, and very different. That lovely hair, the eyes…

'And who are you?' she asked, slowly. Years later, she would remember the first thing she'd noticed about him was that nose.

'I'm Robert Sutherland. Everyone calls me Com.' He hoped she would think that was an interesting answer.

Audrie's eyes widened. There was a pause while they looked at each other.

'Oh, I know who you are. Didn't you step out with Dottie Carberry?'

'That was a long time ago. Yes, we were good chums.' Com felt slightly awkward. 'She must have gone home, what, in thirty-five?'

The party was starting to gather their things and make for the bar. Com realised that they were standing on their own.

'Dottie's a great friend,' Audrie continued. 'She's married now. I had lunch with her about a month before we sailed. She told me about you.'

'Oh, Lord. What else did she say?' Something inside Com told him that more than anything else in the world, he wanted this girl to have heard good things about him.

'She said you took her around, and that you were the most romantic man she'd ever been on a house party with.'

His heart leaped. 'Anything else?'

'Oh, lots. Most of it complimentary. Some not so much.'

'Perhaps we could meet and you can tell me?'

'I'm terribly busy,' she grinned up at him, her blue eyes wide open. 'But you can find me at the Manns. Now I must catch up with them.'

'Of course. But…' Com watched her slim figure walking out into the reception hall, before he turned back to the table to pick up his glass. Anna Maertens was nowhere to be seen.

The Glenugie tea estate, fifteen or so miles south of Maskeliya in the Central Ceylon Highlands and more than four thousand feet above the heat of Colombo, was quietening down in the early evening. Tea pluckers and overseers, finishing work, gradually scattered back down the winding road to their lines. Above them on the hill sat the superintendent's bungalow, with spectacular views over the neat rows of tea bushes to the west, and the small lake a hundred yards below.

The long living room of the bungalow, with its highly polished wooden floors, pot plants and overstuffed chairs, featured an eclectic assembly of furniture, some shipped from Heals store in the Tottenham Court Road, some ordered from Colombo catalogues. Others had been made locally, and some essential items – bookshelves and their contents, including many on the growing and production of tea – had been left behind by the Finch Noyes and other former superintendents and their families.

The current mistress of the estate, Peggy Mann, returning from giving her dinner instructions to the cook, found Audrie, with a woollen cardigan round her shoulders, nestling with her feet under her in an old chintz-covered sofa, reading a travel guide. On the wind-up gramophone behind her on the sideboard, Bing Crosby was crooning *Pennies From Heaven*.

'Would you like some tea? I've asked for a pot. Ham will be in soon. What have you got there?'

Audrie stood up, marking her place and folding the book onto a three-legged side table. The record finished and the needle hissed until she reached over to lift it off.

'It was on the library shelf. Yes, thank you, I'd love a cup. *A Bicycle Tour of the Ceylon Highlands*, dated 1899. It seems to be my Pa's copy. He's noted in the fly to look at page 60; it mentions him as a newly arrived young creeper.'

Audrie looked up at her godmother. 'Auntie Peg, I was wondering. You talked about first meeting Ham when he was on home leave. How did it happen?'

'Yes, darling. It was his second trip home after twelve years here.' Peggy went over to a tall vase of rich dark flowers and started picking off dead heads. 'They used to say the company would only allow a chap to marry when he finished his second tour. And of course, if one wanted to get married, it was very unlikely in those days that one would ever meet anyone suitable out here, so the young men had to find a wife when they were back in England on leave. But what did you want to know?'

'It seems ludicrous. And so unsubtle. How on earth could anyone find a wife in just six months' leave? Did the men go out looking for one? Did Uncle Ham go out looking for a wife or did you two just meet?'

'Well, darling, there were several ways to go about it – and Ham used all of them, bless his heart. Why do you ask?'

'It just seems so unromantic. Going around looking for a wife. D'you think that's why Dads wanted to send me back out here? D'you think he wanted me to find a planter and marry him?'

'I'm sure not. He just wanted you to have a break after all that Edward business.' Peggy smiled at her. 'Didn't Ham ever tell you how we met? I can assure you, darling, it wasn't very romantic.'

'No, go on...' Audrie picked up her cup, and took a sip. 'This smells delicious.'

'Good. Well, you remember I was a trainee nurse?' Peggy paused, smiling to herself at the memory, and adjusted one of the pair of small tortoiseshell combs which held her greying dark hair back from her face.

'Yes, of course.'

'His father, old Colonel Mann,' Peggy went on, 'you know, he'd been in the Indian Army, the Lancers, and officers weren't allowed to get married under the age of thirty in those days.' She sat down on the old sofa and pulled the tea table across. 'They often didn't even have six months, they had perhaps six weeks' home leave, and it was frowned on if you weren't married by the age of thirty-five.'

'Golly. So what did they do? Are these cakes coconut?'

'It became a family joke,' Peggy continued. 'Coconut, yes. A brother officer told him that there was only one place to find the best girls, all sensible types, you know, properly brought up and most suitable for a life in the tropics. The ideal girl could be found in the very nice café opposite the Nurses Home at Guy's Hospital.' She stirred and sipped her tea. 'The story was, of course, all you had to do was to go there at half past twelve, order a cup of coffee or something to eat, read the newspaper and wait around a bit. These young ladies would come in on their break or for lunch, you'd pick the most attractive, think of something charming to say, and Bob's your uncle.'

'Golly. And was that what happened to you?' An elderly yellow Labrador came trotting into the room and sat down next to her, gazing up and thumping his tail on the floor. She reached down to scratch his ears. 'Hello, Oscar. Good boy.'

'Not quite, but near enough. He took one look at Alice, my girl friend and fellow student nurse, and set his cap at her at first. But eventually he saw the light.'

'Talking of seeing the light, I've been wondering about that girl, Anna Maertens, the one Com Sutherland was with when we met. What do you think of her?'

'Well, darling,' Peggy responded carefully. 'She's beautiful, no doubt about that. She attracts attention everywhere she goes. But she seems rootless to me, not quite sure where she's going or what she's doing here.' She stirred her tea. 'She went up to Rangoon last year, some talk about a young man in the Burma Civil. But she was back after only about three months. Why do you ask? Are you seeing him again?'

'Next time we go down, I hope. Oh, probably nothing. Just wondered. Kay Berry and several people have told me she's been out with Com.'

'He has been seen with her, yes, but only a couple of times, last year, dinner parties and that sort of thing. Don't worry. If he's the one for you, it will happen. Mark my words. Anyway, look, here's the post.' She picked up a small pile of envelopes from the tea tray.

'Anything for me?' Audrie turned an eager face up to her godmother.

'Are you expecting anything, some Cargill's catalogues perhaps?' Peggy looked at her in faux innocence, keeping one hand behind her back.

'Don't be daft, of course I am. I'll be furious if Com hasn't written.'

Peggy handed her a blue envelope with a Colombo stamp, depicting a working elephant and the head of King George. 'Here you are. I recognised the writing. It's him. He's quite a catch.'

'Oh goody, let me see.' Audrie picked up a knitting needle to open the envelope. 'But I'm not here to catch anyone.'

Office, Colombo, 30th March 1937
Dearest Audrie
That was a really nice letter, for which thank you.
My feelings on receiving it might be likened to those of an
explorer, lost in the desert and dying of thirst, when someone
suddenly arrives with a bottle of Clicquot 1928. This party
of your aunt Peggy's on Wednesday the 21st is the best news
I've had. Thank you so much for selecting me and I'll be
delighted to come. I'm a spot worried of course, in case I'm
being asked solely for my beautiful dancing.
With my very best wishes,
Robert

'Darling Auntie Peg,' Audrie exclaimed. 'He says he can come to the party, I'll go and write back at once.'

A week later, Com wrote again.

Colombo, 7th April 1937
Your sweet letter was awaiting my return. I'm very
glad to hear you're having a good time strutting around the
countryside but I hope the picnics weren't quite so nice as the
one we had at Mount Lavinia.
I don't know yet when I shall be able to get away in May.
I might not be able to manage it at all, but I'll know better
when I see you on the 20th. Colombo is very quiet and
I'm being most frightfully good, prim and proper. Don't
forget to write soon, with my love, Robert.

As their romance blossomed, the letters became regular, and Robert became Com.

Colombo, 14th April 1937
Have you fixed anything for Tuesday evening? If not, would you like to swim or do anything else? I don't know what time you're coming down but I think the swimming pool would be a grand place to meet you first. It's such an easy place for me to settle any little disputes which may crop up.

By the end of the month they were an item.

Cutler, Palmer, Colombo, 26th April 1937
First of all, thank you for those two wonderful evenings. As I told you before, you really shouldn't be allowed to be such a sweet and adorable creature, because just look at the effect it has on me.
Now listen, we have definitely fixed two bungalow parties during the Coronation. One on the 12th for the Galle Face Coronation Ball and the other on the 15th for the Regimental Ball. So will you please come to them both? I don't know yet when the Buckingham Palace Ball is but I'll let you know as soon as I find out. I'll be in Nuwara Eliya on Friday evening. Do try and get up on Saturday and we will have some fun. Will you please let me know beforehand and lunch with me at the Hill Club? This invitation is extended to whoever comes up with you. I'll be staying at the Grand Hotel so will you please write to me there.

Justice House, Colombo, 5th June 1937

Darling Mums and Dads,

I have a tremendous surprise for you and I hope you will be glad. Robert Sutherland – Com – and I are engaged. We're both too thrilled, and I am writing straight away to tell you and I hope you will say everything is OK.

Com is writing by Tuesday's airmail to you and will you please telegraph as soon as you can to let us know. He is writing and telling you all about himself and his job and everything. He is exactly as much older than I am as the difference between your ages, he is 34 and I am nearly 22.

I am sure you will both like him very much, he is a perfect darling and we've known each other for nearly five months. He comes from Aberdeen and has been out here and in Calcutta just about 12 years. He is General Manager of Cutler Palmer, but I expect he will tell you all that. Darling Mums and Dads, I do hope you are pleased. I came out here with the strongest intention not to get engaged to anyone ever again, but my resolutions don't seem to be much good.

I have had two other proposals so it isn't just the novelty of everything. I do wish you were both out here, too, it would make everything so much easier than having to wait till this letter gets home.

I do hope that you both will think that this is a good thing because I do very much and we are both so frightfully attached to each other. Tons of love to you both

Your loving Audrie

Once they were engaged, the intensity of his letters blossomed, and he was writing to her almost every day.

Cutler, Palmer, Colombo, 1st July 1937

You've just no idea how lonesome I am without you and it's perfectly dreadful darling, and heaven knows what I'm going to feel like when you go home. I just put down the telephone after ringing you up and it's taking lots of willpower not to call you again every five minutes. I'm afraid I'm not feeling very much like this party of Marjorie's this evening. Parties of any description are pretty useless things when you're not there.

Cutler, Palmer, Colombo, 5th July 1937

That was such a marvellous weekend, but the time always goes so mighty quickly when I'm with you that it all feels like a couple of minutes and here I am just now longing and aching for you all over again. Saturday night when we had the bungalow to ourselves, was just the most marvellous night of my life, except perhaps the night when you said you'd marry me. I think that sister of mine wasn't far from the bullseye when she spoke of engagements being a succession of partings, and I'm getting to the stage when I just can't stand them. Even saying Goodnight to you last night, when I was only going to be about 10 yards away from you, was absolute torture.
I am sending off the photograph you asked for today, and one to your mother. Don't forget to advise her, otherwise she'll think it's an advertisement for Austin Reed's and throw it in the fire.

Cutler, Palmer, 8th July 1937

What a lovely letter from you this morning, darling, it made me absolutely whoop with delight, and it took me all my time not to chuck the head clerk under the chin.

I'll probably be hearing from my firm tomorrow, so if I do I'll bring the letter up with me for further plan making. I've got so much to talk to you about this weekend, and so many kisses to give you and so little time. I hope you won't mind if I just start in without saying hello or anything.

Colombo, 14th July 1937

Only two more days before I see you again. I'm still being frightfully good, bed every night at 9.30 but possibly that will alter next week. It will be just grand meeting anew over the eggs and bacon in the morning, in fact I think I shall read my paper at breakfast and give you an insight into the future.

I note your warnings about being on my best behaviour this weekend. Just as well you told me darling otherwise I'd have been sitting with you on my knee, in front of Aunt Peggy, or dipping my bread in the soup or something.

I'll certainly mention the subject of bridesmaids. It would be rather fun having Kay, with Neil as best man – not forgetting of course that you're going to be the bride and I the bridegroom. Let there be no mistake about that darling. In fact when you arrive at the altar I'll have a good peek through the veil to make sure it's you.

Colombo, 16th July 1937

I've written to the firm definitely accepting the postponement of my leave until April 39, so that's another boat burned, whatever happens.

Audrie had originally only come out for six months, and now she would use her return ticket to go home and prepare for their wedding.

Colombo, 2nd September 1937

*Last night saying goodbye on Orontes was pretty grim,
especially when I had to leave the ship, but I am trying
to forget all that now and concentrating on looking forward
to your return.*

*I do hope you've had a decent trip so far. They looked a pretty
lousy lot on board but maybe you've found one or two nice ones.
I was rather amused by the beautiful and loud young person
with the expensive accent we met on Wednesday — he rather
gave the impression that if you weren't perfectly comfortable and
satisfied with everything he would himself choke off the captain.
So?*

Colombo, 6th September 1937

*My darling, it's a nonsense to worry about Anna, there was
nothing between us before I met you and there's nothing now.
You know what a small town Colombo is, and you know how
we all run into everyone all the time. So please don't fret.
Anyway, I played golf yesterday with the Duchess. She was
laying down the law as usual and for about ten minutes she
harangued to me that I must not on any account get married
in the morning. Four-thirty was the one and only time. After
about quarter of an hour I meekly said 'You're wasting your
time, I'm still getting married in the morning,' whereupon she
completely foozled her next shot.*

*I've just had a circular from the Hill Club saying they now
boast a private sitting room so I think we ought to spend a few
days there. I've never sat in a private sitting room but it must
be fun judging by all the fuss they make about it.
Anyway I'll inspect this room when I go there in November.*

Colombo, 22nd September 1937

This very day you arrive at Southampton and it's just as well because my heart strings are already stretched to breaking point and if you had gone another few inches further they would have snapped altogether. I think there's a lot to be said for the good old primitive days. If a chap met a lovely girl then there was none of this hanging about on his part or shooting off to the other ends of the earth on her part. It was merely drag her back into his cave. Civilisation is all very well at times but when it starts messing around with me and my girl it's just no dam' use whatsoever.

I hope you were being faithful last night because if you start flitting around with any of these Kentish snoops, there's going to be warfare on a large scale. Othello was supposed to be a pretty jealous chap, or was it Iago? Well, no matter whoever it was he was a mere amateur handicap 36 compared with me. I'm delighted about these rowing exercises you did on board ship. It's very good for the tummy muscles, but do you know that once you stop rowing, your tummy could go out like a balloon again and your mother will be thinking of sending you discreetly abroad, while your father polishes up his best horse whip.

PO Box 245 Colombo, 27th September 1937

Neil and I had an early dinner and sat talking for hours afterwards discussing the wedding. Grand fun. We even got as far as assigning different jobs to the different ushers. One to look after the cars, another to see that the bridesmaids are properly cared for, another to make frantic signs to the organist when the bride arrives and so forth.

PO Box 245 Colombo, 29th September 1937

I have come to the conclusion thinking things over carefully that I shall make the perfect husband. In fact if they have a competition for perfect husbands next year I shall win it on my head. This is no light statement. Let us, if you like, go into the matter thoroughly, point by point and consider the attributes necessary for perfection:

1. *Physical beauty.* Has it not been said by all the leading authorities that beauty is not only superficial but is totally unnecessary in a husband — and am I beautiful? *Ho! Points to Sutherland 20/20*

2. *Physical fitness.* Am I A1 at Lloyds? Yes. Can I run a mile in 1 minute? No I can't. But who wants a husband who's constantly rushing off and running a mile in one minute? *Points to Sutherland 20/20*

3. *Devotion.* This is my absolute strong suit. You're probably aware of the alleged devotion of a spaniel for its master. Well, stop me if you've heard this one before, but if you take 1000 spaniels and 1000 masters and add up the total of the devotion, multiplied by another 1000, subtract for little Benji when he bit Neil on the leg, and you get somewhere near my devotion to you my sweetie. *Marks 20/20*

4. *Riches.* I may drop a point or two here. You've only got to read your Bible to know that rich folk haven't a hope in hell of entering the kingdom of heaven, and 1200 rupees a month seems a fairish lot to me. May cause St Peter to stop and ponder a bit. But if I hand over all my salary to you darling and let you run the accounts, then I shall be able to tell St Peter that I haven't a bean in the world — nothing in fact but the shirt on my back — Cargill's, 10 rupees. *Marks 20/20.*

I could babble on like this for years but I'm forgetting that out of duty you will have to read it all and so I'll try hard to curb this flowing pen.

Colombo, 4th October 1937

Your three letters from on board ship have arrived. I loved your description of the frightful woman. On every ship that ever sails the high seas there's always someone of that calibre. On my last trip home, we had one, absolutely doped to the eyebrows and never sober, she turned out to be a lesbian actress. On my previous trip out, we had a stunning-looking English woman who got drunk every night and sang at the top of her voice in the smoke room. Beautiful clothes, dazzling jewels, and when we got to Port Said, her husband came on board to meet her, a dusty old Persian, with a fez.

Colombo, 6th October 1937
We had a drinks party at the bungalow last night and invited all the dull sort of people we had to invite – the Harrises, Elliots, Morrises and Leftleys, in fact all the boring or goodie goodie ones, with just a sprinkling of cads to help us through.

Colombo, 28th October 1937
The latest engagement is Brenda Thorpe, to young Archie Trevor. He's a lucky bloke because they're only announcing the engagement on Saturday and are being married in a fortnight. Not, mind you, that I would like to marry Brenda Thorpe in a fortnight, oh no, don't misunderstand me, one man's meal is another man's poison.
I've had a look around for Kay's present, and I will have Siedle make us up a lovely clip in white gold studded with small white sapphires and one blue sapphire in the middle. What do you want for a wedding present, my darling? You can have a diamonda tiara, a pearla necklace, a diamonda broocha or a small bottle of scenta. But the diamonda tiara, the pearla necklacea, diamonda broocha all finish.

Colombo, 20th November 1937
Your Uncle Ham says he is delighted at being asked to give you away. You mustn't worry for a moment about running the bungalow. You'll do it on your head, my darling, and I'll start you off if you like, because I've run bungalows many a time. The easiest thing to do, once we get started, is to compare notes with Bunny or someone and see that we don't get stung and remember that William will be Appu, and entirely responsible.

I am going to keep a book with the names of all people invited, whether they come or not, and a description of each one's present. Then whoever comes to see us afterwards darling we can look up the book, haul the present out of the lumber room, and stick it in some prominent spot.

Colombo, 6th December 1937
Angus is coming along to dinner at Sefton tonight and the four of us may amble along to the Galle Face afterwards and watch the young things enjoying themselves. One of the blokes this morning asked me if I was married, so I said, No, but ring me five weeks today and ask me again. Tomorrow I'm off househunting.

Com left the office early and drove south, past the Galle Face Hotel. Two and a half miles further down, he turned right into Melbourne Avenue.

The Avenue was a fairly rough unpaved road and with just six trees scattered along its four hundred yards of gradual slope between Galle Road and the sea, it hardly yet deserved the title of avenue. Halfway down, Com found the bungalow he'd come to see. It wasn't a bungalow either, but an impressively solid two-story stone house, painted white, and set just fifteen yards back from the road. A large portico supported by solid, square pillars, protruded high above the front door. A covered balcony ran round the entire first floor, below a gently sloping roof which extended well over the windows to protect the rooms from the sun.

A discreet sign on the left entrance gate proclaimed the name *Laverstock*. It must have been built for a Scotsman, reflected Com. A vehicle could drive under the porte cochère, pick up or drop its occupants under shelter from the weather, and head straight out again without turning. Probably designed to take account of the fact that Sinhala drivers were not too hot on reversing.

While he waited for the owners' agent, he scanned up and down the road. There was another new bungalow under construction a hundred yards nearer the sea, and up by the Galle Road corner, two uniformed servants stood talking outside a grand edifice, with palms waving in the gardens and a huge jacaranda hanging over the walls. A European boy in a pith helmet emerged with his ayah from the gate, and as they turned to walk down towards the beach, both the men touched their palms together in greeting to the child. A quiet road, Com noted, in which to start their married life, near the sea, little traffic, and plenty of space for the family when they came along.

Several minutes later, a car turned into the Avenue, and pulled up in a cloud of dust. An English boy, not more than twenty, jumped out to greet him.

'Mr Sutherland? Eric Morris from Cargill's Estates. Pleased to meet you, sir. Sorry to keep you waiting, sir. Let me show you around.'

Com followed the boy to the front door. As he fumbled with the keys, Com noted the tall window frames, set either side of the door. They stepped into a hallway with rooms leading off left and right, and with a curving staircase in the corner.

'Drawing room here,' Morris pointed left, 'dining room through here, facing out to the garden. I'll lead the way, shall I?' Com followed the agent into the drawing room, which was large and airy, with a wooden floor which had been polished to a high shine. Care had obviously been taken to ensure that the maximum light could come into the house, without allowing the direct sunlight which, besides making the rooms uncomfortably warm, would cause all their furnishing materials to fade. In the centre overhead hung a large electric fan.

'Are they fitted everywhere?' Colombo landlords were notoriously mean about installing fans.

'They certainly are, in all the reception rooms and even in the second bedrooms. And of course you and your family will have the advantage of some sea breezes.' Through the side windows Com could see a newly laid lawn, where a garden boy sat on his haunches, gazing at a bed of weeds.

'Will your wife be wanting to see the house as well?' Morris turned to Com.

'She's not my wife yet,' Com replied, smiling at the thought. 'She's on passage out, returns next week. We're to be married at the end of the month.'

'May I offer my congratulations, sir?' Morris shook Com's hand. 'I'm sure this will be the right home for you.' They passed through a double door into the study at the back, which he noted with satisfaction had an entire wall covered in white-painted wooden shelves. Audrie was nearly as voracious a reader as he was, and they always waited impatiently for the newest books to arrive from England at the Apothecaries Bookshop. By the look of it, all his chess and mathematics books would fit in well.

'The kitchen and servants' quarters are through here,' Morris said, opening a small door to the large kitchen area. He stood back, wiping his forehead with a large handkerchief. Com stepped through, and was pleasantly surprised to see a modern kitchen, with many of the usual fittings already in place. Audrie would be thrilled, he thought, but then checked himself and reconsidered. Cook would be thrilled, Audrie would be pleased.

'No Frigidaire?' he asked.

'No, sir. You're expected to provide your own, these days, since the new ones have become much cheaper. Elephant House have the new American Westinghouse in stock, one of our clients at George Steuarts just ordered one for his new flat in Galle Face Apartments.'

'Are the details and measurements all given on the property schedule?' Com asked.

'Certainly, here we are, Mr Sutherland,' Morris handed him a flimsy printed sheet, 'and you'll have seen that all the interior doors are wide for European furniture. And with two bathrooms, that's quite a luxury for the price, if I may say so.'

'Indeed,' Com replied. 'Which reminds me. How much are they asking?'

Morris checked his dossier. 'Asking two ninety-five, sir.' Com paused for five seconds, and then made up his mind.

'Mr Morris, advise your client I'll take it, first of the month. I'll need everything cleaned again, no dust or insects, and not an Anna more than two seventy-five a month. Five years with a break option after three. Let me know this evening.'

Two weeks later, on the steps outside St Peter's Garrison Church, Colombo, Audrie gazed steadily at the camera, with an expression of serenity.

She wore a dress of white ciré satin, with long white sleeves and a high neckline embroidered with pearls, and carried a huge bouquet of stephanotis. She was tilting her head back, and her chic bob, her elegance and air of tranquillity seemed at odds with Com's relaxed stance, in his standard formal tropical outfit, the white double-breasted gabardine suit, two-tone shoes, and with his wide, toothy grin.

Half-hidden behind Audrie stood her bridesmaid, Kay Berry, in a slinky dress of the same ciré material, with flowers in her hair and in her hands. Next to Com, turning his profile to camera, was his best man, Neil Garland, with his long chin, high forehead, narrow, aristocratic face and large dark moustache.

Com and Audrie moved into Laverstock the week after they returned from their honeymoon.

'Have you seen the Bungalow Book?' Audrie paused halfway out of the bedroom door. Com stood in front of his dressing stand, fiddling with his cufflinks.

'On my desk, on top or under some papers or the blotter. That looks lovely, darling.'

She wore a short-sleeved white cotton dress, with a thin black belt and two rows of black buttons down the back. Her hair was pinned up, to keep her neck cool.

'Thank you. Does this look too smart? I'm meeting Kay for lunch at the Swimming Club. I can't go on wearing this for much longer, my tummy is beginning to expand.' She smoothed her hands over the thin fabric.

'Nonsense, you're only two months, still as slender as the day we met. Are you doing the accounts this morning?'

'I'm going to have a go. Peggy says I should always do it myself otherwise I'll never understand what goes on in my own house. But she says it takes ages and the bills never seem to add up.'

'Righto. Spot on as usual,' Com replied. 'Rather you than me, I'd be thrilled if you took over. I often spend the whole day staring at accounts, and it's the last thing I want to do when I get back from office. Go on down, darling, I'll be there in a tick, and then I've to be at the port at eight thirty.'

Audrie's heels tapped on the dark teak as she started downstairs. In Com's study, she picked up the accounts book from his desk and then opened the side door to the verandah, where the breakfast table awaited her. Outside, the scent of that jasmine, Queen of the Night, remained in the garden, merging with the ozone from the waves breaking on the shore a hundred yards down the avenue. The Appu, in his long white tunic, placed a glass of mango juice and a plate of papaya and lime in front of her place, and turned towards her with a slight bow of his head.

'Good morning, Lady, I hope you slept well.'

'Good morning, William, yes, very well, thank you.' After four months she had managed to settle into a comfortable relationship with William. To begin with, she had worried that she might sound too distant, and had over-reacted. Com had warned her not to become too friendly. But now, she was no longer nervous instructing him on what she wanted, and William, too, had settled into his new environment, no longer regarding his master's new wife as an extra inconvenience around his domain.

'Is fan working satisfactorily, Lady?'

'Yes, it's much cooler now, well done. In time for the monsoon. How is everyone?'

'Everything fine, thank you, Lady.' He pulled out a chair for her to sit, and then stood back. 'Cook is settling in.' She watched as he carefully squeezed wedges of lime onto the papaya. She wasn't quite sure about cook.

'Would Lady like anything else afterwards, please? Perhaps an egg hopper?'

'Not for me, thank you, William, the fruit and tea will be all I need. Let me know how cook gets on. Master will be down in a minute.' William poured her a cup of tea, and vanished quietly in the direction of the kitchen. From outside, a torrent of shrieks from the bird population announced the arrival of the garden boy.

The first time she had opened the Bungalow Book, and seen the pages of columns of figures covering all their household expenditure, she had felt a migraine coming on and had shut it immediately. Copies of this foolscap hardcover notebook were handed out free every year by the sponsors to every expatriate household in Ceylon. Alongside blank pages for each month and each item of expenditure, householders could enjoy advertisements for such essential items as the New Meter-Miser Frigidaire, Armour Cleansing Powder, Izal disinfectant and Solignum Wood Preservative – 'destroys white ants'.

The next time, she had lasted slightly longer before breaking out in a sweat, but now, four months later, she was beginning to understand the entries and to see where all the money went.

With fork in hand, Audrie squeezed more lime onto the papaya, and opened the accounts book to the page headed *Expenditure for the Month of July, 1938*.

Cooks Account. Elephant House account, that was dairy and bakery, *Servants wages.* The book had ready-printed headings for a huge list of servants. Surely people couldn't still have that many? Who on earth still employed a dressing boy, or sewing woman these days? She scanned down the list and added up their wages bill.

Appu, 45 Rupees, Cook, 35 Rs, that was a lot for someone she wasn't sure of yet, House Coolie 28 Rs, Kitchen Coolie, he was lovely, always smiling, 15 Rs, Dhobi, 40 Rs, Messenger, 15 Rs, Chauffeur, she was rather frightened of him, 30 Rs, and the sweet but lazy Garden Boy, she was sure he was William's son or nephew, 5 Rs. She totted the figures up, that was two hundred and thirteen.

'You should learn how to use an abacus.' Com pushed the mosquito door open and sauntered over to the table, tossing his white jacket over the spare chair, and kissed the back of her neck.

'Wouldn't help. You know I hate maths in any form,' she said, as he sat and poured his cup of tea. 'How much will we pay the nanny?'

'Twenty-five rupees. She's earning twenty a month with the Nelsons and we agreed to bump it up when Bunny gave her such a glowing reference. But she won't start until the baby's nearly due. How much does it all come to?' He started eating his breakfast.

Audrie frowned at the long list and ran her finger down the column. 'I make it two hundred and thirteen now, and so when the baby comes, two hundred and thirty eight with Nanny. Does that sound right?' She read out all the salaries again and Com nodded, his mouth full.

'Mm. Well done. You can forget about the abacus. Where will you go with Kay?'

'We're going shopping, to Millers first, she wants more sheets, and she's promised to take me to the Swimming Club for lunch.'

'I'll send the car back. And if I can, I could join you there. I'll see how it goes.'

A quarter of an hour later, outside the bungalow, Audrie kissed her husband, and watched him drive up Melbourne Avenue. She waved as he turned the corner onto Galle Road, and then returned to the veranda, where the Bungalow Book lay threatening her. Already, the day was warming up. With a small sigh, she picked up the first of a pile of cooks' chits.

Half an hour later, as she was cross-checking their bill from Elephant House, the telephone rang on the desk beside her. She picked it up:

'Hello, four three four seven.'

'Hello. May I speak to Com, please?' A woman.

'Who's calling?' Audrie didn't recognise the voice.

'It's Anna Maertens; is that Audrie?'

Her throat tightened. 'Anna, yes, hello. No, he's left for the office, is there a message?'

'No, don't worry. No matter. See you soon. Bye.' The line was disconnected.

What could she want, thought Audrie. Why would she be calling Com at ten in the morning? What had really happened between them? Where was she calling from? Wasn't she supposed to have taken passage to Rangoon again?

It was so difficult when everyone she met in Colombo seemed to know about Com's past.

─────────────

At this time of year, it usually rains every day, thought Com, as he ran from the office door and jumped back into the car, throwing his suit jacket across the passenger seat. And if you're not soaked by the rain, you'll be soaked in sweat.

Even with the windows wide open, the July heat, between the incessant showers, was sticky and oppressive. As Com drove the Austin down Galle Road it felt like an oven with a fan blowing at him, and the leather seat stuck to the back of his shirt. On the road, rickshaws and ox carts mingled with the few cars, while the usual crowds of walkers and bicyclists wore hoods and heavy capes, as though the heavens were about to open again any minute.

He slowed down to turn right into Melbourne Avenue, and waited as a bicycle with father pedalling, mother and a small baby perched on the crossbar, crossed in front of him. A hundred yards down, as he nosed the car into the gates of the bungalow, the front door opened, and William stepped out towards the car, pressing his palms together below his chin.

'*Ayubowan.* Good evening, Master.' William held the car door open.

'Good evening, thank you, William.' As they stepped into the hallway, William picked up a pair of silver tongs from the side table, selected a small flannel, dipped it in a bowl of scented water and offered it to Com. He held it to his face for a few seconds, tossed it back and followed through to the sitting room, just as Audrie appeared in the doorway to greet him.

'I thought I heard the car.' Audrie kissed him and took his hand to lead him into the centre of the room. 'Thank you, William. How was today? You look a little tired.'

'It's just the heat.' Com picked up a letter which was waiting for him on a silver tray. 'Monsoon will be over soon and then it'll cool down. Everyone's at half-cock.' He laid the jacket on a side table and lowered himself into a planter's chair, his long legs extended.

'And how's the wonderful world of Cutler's?' Audrie re-arranged the vase of frangipani on the coffee table.

'Good in the office, thank you, although we've found rot in the roof at Prince Street,' Com smiled. 'Fair to middling at the warehouse. Not bad in the shops. Hotel business better than ever. I promoted Andrews to be the new shop manager. He works well and is ready for more responsibility. But it's all a bit slow in this heat. Now, I need a long drink.'

'Whisky?'

'It's a little early. Just a cold glass of 'Polly, darling, please.'

'Of course, anything for my darling hot husband.' Her heels tapped on the polished wooden floor as she hurried to a side table in the corner of the room, where a large bottle of Apollinaris mineral water lay in an ice bucket beside a drinks tray, with a plate of lime slices. A large fan hummed slowly over the table. Outside, she could see the garden coolie contemplating a bush he had spent the last hour trimming. It didn't look much different to her. She had been waiting all day to ask about Anna but now didn't seem the right time.

'How was your lunch with Kay?'

'She was on great form, and looked wonderful.' Audrie prised off the seal, poured him a long glass and dropped in two wedges of lime. 'She expects to be proposed to any time soon. Being in love does wonders for your skin, even out here. But darling...'

'Neil hasn't said anything to me, but knowing him he wouldn't,' Com interrupted. He took a long swallow and fitted the glass into the hole in the armrest. 'That's better. He's keeping it all very close to his chest.'

'We'll see them tonight; I'm sure he'll be down on one knee any day now.'

'And the famous household accounts? Are you now the mistress of all you survey?'

'I think I've mastered it, at last,' Audrie replied, as she perched on the edge of the sofa, carefully folding the skirt beneath her. 'It took me an hour, which is a new record. Last time was one hour and a quarter. And, it came out right first time. The Elephant House bill was wrong. How would they dream we would ever order Snoflake bread? They must be mad.'

'What did you do? Call the manager?' Com put on his serious face.

'I wrote them a note pointing out their mistake and sent a cheque for the right amount.'

'Well done. That'll show 'em.'

'Don't tease. Darling, you have remembered it's JC and Vi's 25th anniversary dinner tonight? I've told William we're out, and cook has a night off.' She returned to the drinks tray and refilled her glass with soda.

'It was in my office diary. I remembered just in time and ate a very small lunch. I'm so glad we're going. They've been so kind and it's grand that you and Kay get on so well.'

'She was the best bridesmaid a girl could want. Apparently she's organising tonight. And she'll be wearing the brooch we gave her.'

He finished the drink. 'Shall we have the windows open, move the air around before it starts to get dark? What time are they expecting us?'

'The usual, about eight I'd say. It will be smart. William's pressed your evening coat.' She opened the doors onto the terrace, and the air outside seemed to have cooled down. She pulled the gauze screen across to prevent flying insects coming to the light. 'It'll soon start raining again. Another? With something in it this time?'

'I'll wait. Must be kind to my kidneys. Who's going to be there?'

'Mostly people you know, I'd say. Certainly Neil. And of course, Ham and Peggy. Vi said probably a few of JC's legal colleagues. A few planter chums.' She turned on the two table lights, creating a warm glow in the darkening room. 'And, she says there's a visiting admiral, the new one taking over as deputy C-in-C, and his wife, apparently he's an old chum of JC. Now, you relax, it won't take me more than half an hour to get ready.'

'I'm sure it'll be grand. Your first big Colombo dinner. I'll give John the night off as well and we can drive ourselves. You're not nervous?'

'A little. I hope I won't find myself talking to the admiral. Men's uniforms always confuse me. And is a commander more important than a captain?'

'You'll be fine, darling. In case of any doubt, count the rings. When they look at you, they'll forget their own names anyway. Go on up. I'll have a shower and stay out of your way.'

'I've ironed the long cream silk but you must tell me if you can see through it. I might need an extra slip.' Audrie put down her glass and bent over the chair to kiss him. Com snaked an arm around her legs and held her there for a few long seconds.

Audrie couldn't put her question off any longer. 'Darling, Anna Maertens called today, after you left. What does she want with you?'

'Anna? Oh, my darling. Why did she call?'

'That's what I want to know. If you don't mind.' Audrie knew it was probably nothing. But she'd been fretting all day. What if he was having an affair?

'My angel, she's in the cast of the new dramatic society production, and assistant producer. She wants me in it but I'm too busy.'

'Why didn't you tell me? As long as she's not still chasing after you?'

'Don't be a silly. It was never anything, just a dance.' He stood up and took her face in his hands to kiss her. 'Now hurry up. I'll miss you.' She set off to change. Com leaned back in his chair, listening to her steps on the stairs, and thought about all the wasted years before Audrie had come into his life.

Upstairs, Audrie felt relieved, but still, even if Com thought nothing of it, there was no knowing what Anna was really up to. She would keep a watch out.

As befitted the Chief Justice of Ceylon, Sir James Berry, his wife, Violet, and their three daughters lived in the grandest residential area of Colombo, Torrington Square. Justice House may have been called a bungalow, but was in reality a large mansion. Lights shone from every window of the house, and outside many of the trees in the wide gardens were illuminated, creating a magical atmosphere even on this damp evening.

As they came to the entrance Com waited for the door to be opened for Audrie and then hopped out. The Appu waved to a boy who stepped forward to park the car.

'Good evening, Manel. Are you keeping well?'

'*Ayubowan*, Master and Lady. Please to go on inside.'

Across the wide candlelit hallway, their hosts stood at the doorway of their drawing room, ready to greet their guests.

'Audrie, Com, the glamorous newlyweds.' Lady Berry stepped forward to welcome them. 'Thank you for coming. Audrie, how lovely you look.'

'Thank you,' she replied, blushing. 'Many congratulations, Vi, Or should we congratulate the lucky husband?'

'Anyway, Happy Silver Anniversary, JC and Vi,' Com butted in. 'We both wish you many more happy years together.' Audrie knew that Berry had become a particular friend of Com's over the years since his arrival in Colombo, and that her husband regarded him as a mentor.

'The first twenty years are the hardest,' Sir James smiled. 'You'll soon get used to it. Go on in, you'll know practically everyone.' Audrie picked up her long skirt, took her husband's arm, and together they stepped into the drawing room. It was already busy with the chatter of a dozen or so people; a steward approached them bearing a tray containing glasses of gin or whisky, while a second offered ice, tonic water or soda. Audrie took the smallest gin she could see and asked for it to be topped up with tonic.

'Don't forget rule six,' Com whispered. 'If you use up all your small talk on the first man you meet, you're bound to find yourself next to him at dinner.'

'Not a chance,' Audrie leaned towards him. 'I shall chat to the women only, and start with Peggy, of course. Off you go, darling.' Com set out for the far side of the room where he had spotted Neil Garland. As Audrie turned, she nearly bumped into a tall, sandy-haired but deeply tanned man with a familiar face, who stared at her for a second.

'It's Audrie Finch Noyes, isn't it? Charlie Burrows. We met on the quay when you came in on *Orontes* with the Manns.'

'Gosh yes, I do remember, with Ham and Peggy. Hello again. I'm Sutherland now. I'm sure you know Com, my husband, over there?' She sipped her gin and felt a little glow of confidence.

'Of course, I read about the wedding, very grand affair. Peggy and Ham invited us, so sorry I couldn't make it.'

'So were we,' she assured him, now embarrassed that she hadn't remembered whether he'd been at their wedding or not. 'But, Charlie, how are you? Down for business? How is Michael St, St thingummy getting on?' Dammit, she could never remember his name.

'Just a few days. Wouldn't miss the party. Staying at the Blackwoods. Michael? It's de St Aubin. He's fine. Doing well. I think Mike rather fell in love with you on the passage, he talked of nothing else for days.'

'Oh, I don't know…' She lowered her eyes, feeling another blush coming on. 'That's a bit strong. You know how it is at sea. We just talked. It was his first passage, wasn't it? But,' she remembered, 'he certainly was a lovely dancer. It must be, what, eighteen months now?' Now Burrows was staring over her shoulder again and she glanced round to see an attractive woman with a striking pale face and long dark hair arriving at the door, to be immediately surrounded by two young men.

'Oh, Mike, he's fine,' Burrows said, gazing at the new arrival. 'But there's Anna Maertens. You don't see many sights like that up-country, I'll say.'

So that's her, Audrie thought, as she turned again to stare across the room.

'Sweet girl. But typical,' Burrows went on. 'Nothing to do all day, and then she's always late.' He caught himself staring and tuned back to Audrie. 'Mike's still on his first tour, doing well. They love him on the estate, and his Tamil is improving every week.'

The Maertens girl passed them by, now with a drink in her hand and a young man on her arm. She really is as beautiful as they say, Audrie thought. She wondered again exactly what had gone on between Anna and Com. Burrows gazed over his glass at Anna, then turned back to her. 'But tell me, what of my dear old Finch? How's he getting on, now he's changed his topee for a bowler?'

She grinned up at Burrows. 'Still up at dawn, can't stop him. He's become a commuter, catches the 7.50 to London Bridge. He's deputy chairman now. My mother wants him to slow down, but he's busier than ever.' She paused. Since her return to Ceylon, Audrie had learned with increasing pride how much her father had been loved and respected by the British tea trade community, and she was starting to see him in a completely new light. 'Look, Charlie, I must catch Peggy before we go in. Excuse me.'

'Of course. Give Finch my best when you write.'

'And mine to Michael.'

'I will. Perhaps he can come to call on you two when he is down next time. He doesn't know anyone in Colombo.'

'Of course. Kay and I can take him to lunch. Tell him to get in touch, he can write to Com at Cutler's.' Audrie fluttered her fingers at him as he set off in pursuit of Anna Maertens. Now, there must have been at least twenty people in the room, and she could see her husband talking to two women she recognised. Not applying rule six, she thought. The steward approached her with a tray of refills, and she was about to take a gin when she decided to wait.

As she gazed around her, she saw that she was in one of the most beautiful private houses in Colombo. Not overcrowded even when full of people, the long, high-ceilinged drawing room contained some exquisite furniture, arranged to perfection, a few rugs on the highly polished floors, and a remarkable collection of paintings, mostly of Ceylonese subjects, including a striking picture of a Buddhist monk in his brilliant orange robes, against a dark background, and another of the Perahera festival in Kandy, with gorgeous elephants dressed overall in gold.

Peggy was at the centre of a group of several other guests, and as Audrie was introduced, she found they all were already well aware of who she was. Everyone either knew Com, had heard of their marriage, or remembered her own father. They certainly all knew each other very well, which made her feel an outsider. So many new faces were all very confusing. As she tried to memorise all the names, she found herself thinking about Dale Carnegie's *How to Win Friends and Influence People* which, along with every good new book, had arrived from the Apothecaries library a few weeks before. To remember names, it had said, you had to associate each face with an animal, or was it a tree? The man in front of her, with small, beady eyes, and a thin, turned-up nose, looked a bit like a rhino.

She finally touched Peggy's arm and they moved to one side to speak privately. 'Darling Audrie, how are you?' she asked. 'Everything all right at home?'

'Couldn't be better. Peggy, he is wonderful, so kind even though I know nothing and I'm completely useless in the house with the servants.'

Peggy tilted her head back and laughed. 'Don't be silly, you'll soon get the hang of it all.'

'I do hope so. I miss him all day and can't wait for the evening,' Audrie confessed. 'Monday morning is the worst, when we've been together all weekend and then he goes off to his office and it's just me and the staff. But the other women have been very generous, I'm invited to lunch and to bridge at their clubs, very charming but it's all slightly unreal.'

'And the bungalow?'

Audrie giggled. 'Learning to run a house is a *cauchemar*. I can't imagine how you or Mums ever did it, especially up-country with no shops nearby. You were real heroines! Every day the servants ask me for instructions and I've no idea what to tell them.' They stepped apart for a moment as another guest squeezed between them.

'The first few months, that was the worst part. I was convinced the servants spent all day telling each other what a useless wife I was for their master. I'm sure they were all laughing at me.'

'Darling girl.' Peggy pushed her hair back and took a rather large drink from her glass of gin. 'It's the same for everyone. Don't believe all that Somerset Maugham nonsense.'

'But how do I instruct the cook when I don't know what he's making? I have no idea what goes on in there when I go to see them.'

Peggy laughed. 'Take a tip. If I were you I'd make a point of never going anywhere near the kitchen.'

'But Mrs Churton Walker says in her book you should go in the kitchen every day, at a different time, so you can be sure they keep it clean.'

'You mean in that old Appu book?' Peggy touched her hair again. 'Twenty years ago, maybe. Today, with all these modern appliances, you needn't worry. I remember her. Poor old Churton, it must have been like being married to Boadicea.'

Three newly arrived guests approached them, and chatted about nothing very much until Kay emerged from the dining room door carrying a glass of gin, waved and worked her way over.

'Darling Aud, you look wonderful, how are you?' she asked as they stepped away from the group.

'You too. You're such a heroine, organising all this. How's it going in there?' Audrie nodded towards the dining room.

'Don't ask,' Kay whispered. 'I've had to change the seating again, since we're two short. And Mum's just told cook she wants him to wear his best clean apron, so we're waiting.'

'I saw that Anna Maertens woman,' Audrie confided,' the one Com used to step out with. What do you think of her tonight?'

'She's certainly a head-turner. My Pa thinks she's very bright too. I've put her next to Charlie and we'll see what develops. We're just about ready.' She scuttled back into the crowd. The butler announced dinner, and suddenly Com's friend Neil Garland appeared at her side. He looked even taller and more distinguished in evening dress.

'Audrie, my dear, there you are. Kay's been assisting her mother with the arrangements. I'm to take you in.'

'Oh, goodie, Neil, what a relief. I've met so many new people I don't think I could remember any more names.'

She tucked her evening bag under her elbow, picked up her long skirt and took his arm. Gradually the guests proceeded across the hall and into the dining room. Highly polished silver and glass gleamed in the light of hundreds of candles burning overhead and in candelabra along the length of the table. On the far wall, above Sir James' chair, a portrait of the new king beamed down at them.

There were eleven places on each side, with at least half a dozen servants standing against the walls. At the top of the table, Sir James seemed slightly ill at ease, glancing round the room as he talked with a distinguished-looking woman in dark blue. Charlie Burrows, now with Anna Maertens on his arm, moved past them to stand by a chair further along.

'Very impressive,' Neil murmured, as they arrived at their places. *Mrs R. W. Sutherland* was printed on a white card, set inside a silver pomegranate covered in intricate Kandyan carving. Audrie noticed with some panic that there were five different forks on the left of her place setting. She looked around to see Com escorting Kay to places just across the table from her. Then, she felt a sense of great relief as the genial bulk of Ham Mann appeared on her right, and introduced his companion as Gertie Larsen.

'That's her husband, young Larsen, over there, next to Peggy,' Ham nodded up the table. 'And that's the admiral's wife, Lady

Patricia Ramsay, with JC. Met her yesterday. She's the one who used to be a princess.'

So that's Gertie, Audrie thought as glanced along the table. She knew Gertie Larsen was an old friend of Com's and was also now recently married. Tall and with a lean, brown face and wearing a dark green dress which fell around her ankles, she seemed very relaxed, smiling and laughing with Ham. There must be several of Com's former girlfriends in Colombo, she realised. At least two of them here tonight. When she had read *Rebecca*, a month before, it had made her think about Com's years in Colombo before they'd met. After finishing it, she'd worried for several nights that a mysterious earlier girlfriend would appear in their lives and ruin her happiness.

Finally, the room became silent as Lady Berry arrived on the arm of what Audrie realised must be the admiral, and took their seats at the end of the table. As she sat, so other servants stepped forward to pull out the chairs for the women and seat them. The men took their places, the noise resumed, and conversation buzzed once again.

'Have you heard about Vera?' said Neil, as they served the first course, a dark-coloured soup, and a butler poured her a glass of fino alongside it.

'Vera? The one who runs your chummery? Is this mock turtle?' Audrie looked nervously at her plate.

'Not sure.' He took a cautious sip. 'Tastes real to me. Vera's causing us all much amusement. The Colombo amateur dramatic company are going to do *Interference*, and they've asked Vera to take a tiny part.' Audrie started her soup, filling the spoon only halfway so as not to risk spilling any.

'I read about it. *When a first husband turns out not to be dead, and shows up at the doctor's surgery, blackmail leads to murder.* Who will she be? Not the heroine surely at her age?'

'No fear,' Neil answered. 'It's the part of a sewing woman and she comes on in the second act for exactly five minutes and speaks altogether about a dozen lines. And heavens the fuss.' He dabbed at his moustache with the huge linen napkin. 'It really is a lark. She stamps around the bungalow reading her lines, the whole twelve of them, and when people ring up wanting her to play golf or bridge it's a case of "So sorry, dear, but I think I've got a rehearsal on that date."'

'Hasn't she done this before? At school or something?' Audrie said, while she tried to remember if she should tip the soup plate away from her or to the side. She was supposed to have learned all this at Miss Randall's in Eastbourne.

Neil had noticed. 'It's away from you. No, she never has. And I'm now certain that Vera has been nursing a secret ambition all her life to be an actress and now that her great chance has come, not even the fact that in her little scene she has to play opposite the dreadful Mrs Bancroft seems to deter her. The only thing that worries me is that her enthusiasm being so great, other people will be laughing too, including Mrs Bancroft. That won't be quite so funny.'

Audrie placed her spoon carefully down and took a sip of the sherry. She was beginning to feel much more relaxed. 'Isn't Anna Maertens in it as well? I heard she's quite an actress.'

Neil raised an eyebrow. 'Anna? Yes, she plays the doctor's wife. She's very good, she's been in quite a few productions.' Audrie glanced over at Miss Maertens, who, spoon in hand, was shaking her head at Charlie Burrows.

Once again, Audrie found herself thinking about Com's life in Colombo before she'd met him. 'She's certainly interesting-looking. Did you know her when Com was seeing her? Kay told me they had been friends.'

Neil shook his head. 'Nothing to say. They met at a dance up in Nuwara Eliya. Years ago. Before he and I shared in Sefton together. Not a girlfriend, they just dined and danced.'

He picked up his sherry glass and raised it to her before taking a sip. 'This is delicious. But I think there could be something going on now with Charlie, he's very keen on her. About time too, for him, he's a good man and deserves to find someone after so many years alone up-country. Anna was planning to go on to her people in Burma but stayed on when they met. She's very interested in him, I'd say. But she may not be the settling kind. We'll see.'

Audrie took another look at Anna who was now gazing across

the table at Com. Neil was right, she concluded, but she'd better keep an eye on Miss Maertens. The soup plates were removed and a fish course was circulated, while butlers moved around with a white wine. Audrie remembered she should turn to her neighbour as each course was served, and was about to turn to Ham on her left, but he was finishing a story and laughing with his other neighbour.

She gazed around the table, watching Com now conversing with Kay and the woman on his left, and for a while, she didn't notice what was put in front of her. When she looked down at her fish, it wasn't the food she noticed but the plate underneath. It seemed familiar. Plain white, with a gold frieze border and a simple decoration of roses and berries. She suddenly realised. They were just like her own. They must be her own, the ones she had chosen herself in London. She tapped Neil's elbow anxiously, and he turned back to her.

'Neil, what's this?' She didn't know whether to laugh or be angry. 'These are our plates. They came from London. A wedding present from Com's sister. How on earth did they get here? What's happening?' She turned to Ham on her right and started to push her chair back, but Neil put his hand on her arm.

'Don't worry, dearest Audrie,' Neil tried to calm her down. 'It's just the servants borrowing from each other.'

'What on earth? What do you mean? I know nothing about this!'

Neil leaned over towards her. 'Probably their staff didn't have a perfect set of twenty-four and they rang around to borrow some. Because you're the most recently married, they must have guessed that none of yours were broken yet. It happens all the time. Very Ceylon.'

'Oh, Lord. Why didn't they tell me?' She relaxed back into her chair, much relieved but also slightly embarrassed to have nearly caused a fuss. 'I'm so glad I'm next to you. But don't they ask first? William didn't say anything.'

'They wouldn't normally bother you. I'm sure they'll all be back at Laverstock in the morning.' He picked up his knife and fork. 'Come on, it's delicious,' he encouraged her, 'especially on these plates.'

Audrie turned to her right, where soon Ham was recounting his and Peggy's plans for the cottage they'd bought in Dorset for their retirement. Once they'd enjoyed the fish, and she had watched in concern as her plates were being cleared away, there was a brief lull in the conversation. Sir James, at the end of the table, stood up and tapped his glass with his fork. Everyone stopped talking and turned towards him.

'No, no,' he insisted. 'I'm not making a speech. But I am aware that many of you insist on not smoking before the loyal toast, and many others can't stop for more than a few minutes. So I intend to solve this by asking you all to raise your glasses.' He turned round to face the portrait on the wall behind his place and raised his glass.

'Ladies and Gentlemen, The King.'

Audrie looked left and right. There was a scramble as twenty-three chairs were pushed back, twenty-three glasses were raised, and everyone turned to the portrait, responding: 'The King, God Bless Him.'

As the guests settled back down, Sir James looked down the table at his wife, who gave a firm nod. He turned to the servant at his side, and announced, 'And now, Manel, ask cook to serve the beef.'

A minute later, at the far end of the room, double doors were thrown open and a small figure entered from the kitchen, bearing a huge silver salver upon which lay an enormous sirloin of beef. The cook was wearing a starched hat, with a long white apron. Audrie could see his brown sandaled feet taking slow and nervous steps as, accompanied by the butler, he set out off down the room towards the far end of the table. There was a murmur of appreciation as everyone watched the stately procession.

Finally, the cook arrived at the huge mahogany sideboard, and turned his back to the dining table, to place the dish for carving. Audrie's jaw dropped. She started to giggle, but then shut her mouth abruptly. There was a general intake of breath in twenty-three throats as everyone saw what Audrie had seen. The cook wore nothing under the apron, not even any underwear, and his back gleamed in the candlelight. There was a pause as everyone waited to see what would happen next. Audrie heard a few muffled snorts, and nudged Neil.

Then an unmistakeable voice spoke out. 'Thank you, Ravindu. Well done. That will be all.' From the end of the table, Lady Berry was looking straight at her cook. She sounded very stern, but Audrie could see that she was crying with laughter.

Ravindu turned back towards the table and bowed his head. 'Yes, my Lady.' He set off back towards the kitchen, his bare bottom visible to all. Audrie tore her gaze back to the table, and immediately saw that everyone else had done the same. Some held their napkins to their faces, and across from her, Kay was laughing helplessly while Com searched in his pockets for a hanky. 'Mum said to wear his best apron,' she mouthed at Audrie.

Audrie nodded back at her, and stared across the table, until Com caught her eye, shrugged and raised his eyes to the ceiling. She turned to Neil and murmured, 'Is this what you meant by very Ceylon?'

After dinner, the guests of honour having left for Government House, there was to be a concert of gramophone records, weather permitting, on the lawn beyond the terrace. Audrie re-joined Com as the party trooped outside, and with the remaining guests, they settled in a semicircle of long chairs. The Berrys' Appu stood by the wind-up machine to put on the first disc, and as the concert began with Mozart, conversation dropped away. There was nothing for them to do, after a delicious dinner, except sit back in the heavy heat of the Colombo night, with another fresh cold drink at their side, and listen to the music. Between the records, crickets chirped across the lawn while the tall palms now stood motionless in the tropical moonlight.

After four or five records, Audrie noticed a gentle snoring from the chair beside her. For Com, the combination of a long day, the dinner, the music, that heat and the recumbent position had sent him straight to sleep. She shook his arm to wake him gently, and they clambered to their feet to make their goodbyes.

The Joseph Fraser Nursing Home, Colombo, 2nd January

Darling Mums and Dads,
Here we are at last, Robin Hamish Sutherland and myself. He really is rather a lamb. Eight pounds fourteen ounces when he arrived and 24 inches, really rather large. He has dark curly hair and brown eyes just like Com, but I think he's going to have a Finch Noyes nose. It does make me laugh to think of you two as grandparents, almost as much as Com and I being Papa and Mamma. I can't wait to show him to you when we come back on leave. I'm planning everything now and we'll come to you from Tilbury in April, and then in August go on up to Scotland to Com's people.
The birth wasn't as bad as you thought, but I nearly went crackers listening to the brain-fever birds making that eerie call all night outside my window. And, some very good news, Com has been told that when we return from home leave, he'll be elected to the Cutler, Palmer board as MD and they will increase his salary by Rs 250 a month.
Com's old friend Gertie Larsen and of course Kay have been wonderful helping me over the last few weeks, and we are going to ask them both to be his godmothers and Com wants Neil and Nelly Nelson to be godfathers. Would you tell Chim I want her to be a godmother too, even if she can't be here for the christening? I'm sure she'll be a wonderful Auntie.
Can't wait to show you your grandson
With all my love, Audrie

She looked down at the cot where her son lay fast asleep, put her pen down on the bed tray and sank back into the pillows. Being pregnant in Colombo during the hot weather had not been ideal. For the last month she had been confined to the bungalow, with regular visits from the GP Dr Van Langenberg.

What kind of life would this little boy lead, she wondered? She and Com had discussed their family's future many times, but she still couldn't look forward much beyond their life here in Ceylon. Eventually, of course, they'd go back home to England, in what, maybe seven years when it was time for the little one to start school. But with the excellent news of Com's appointment to the board, wouldn't they be better off financially, staying in Ceylon for a while longer? She couldn't bear the idea of Robin being in Britain at school while she was still out in Ceylon, it'd be like Ham and Peggy's family, they wouldn't see him for years. The old ways would have to change. Besides, should they send him to a Scottish school to be near Com's people in Aberdeen – Com had suggested Fettes – or one near Sussex, where her own parents lived?

Enough of all this, she told herself, lots to do. She picked up the pen again to write to her sister, Chim, about the baby.

Orontes, April 1939

Looking across at her husband and at the baby, sleeping in the sea-cot under his embroidered Orient Line bed sheet, Audrie felt happier then she could ever remember. They were finally on their way for their home leave. They hadn't appeared for dinner the first night, preferring to have a snack in the cabin, while they settled in, but now they had to face the rest of the passengers and start the usual process of a three-weeks-on-board acquaintance.

'It's all right for you, no sleeves. We boys have to wear this rig for dinner every night.' April was not the most comfortable month during which to travel the Indian Ocean, especially as they approached Aden and the Red Sea. Com, in a white tropical dinner jacket, was re-tying his bow tie for the third time.

'At least you don't have to dress up like the poor crew,' Audrie observed. 'Did you see the officers at the reception? Stiff boiled shirts, wing collars, white monkey jackets, waistcoats, the full uniform, in this heat. D'you want me to do that up for you?'

'As long as you come and stand here and do it in the mirror.'

'Silly boy,' she giggled. 'I can't reach or see round you from there. And it's too hot for any of that.'

'Just you wait 'til we get into the Mediterranean,' Com laughed. 'Is he asleep?'

'For the moment. I'll have to feed him again at ten. Flo arranged for the nursery stewardess to sit with him while we have dinner.'

'You can relax for once. There's no need to hurry back.' He rang the service bell, and two minutes later, the nursery stewardess arrived, Com picked up his son from the little cot, and walked along the row of cabins with her to leave him in the nursery, where she and a colleague were supervising several other babies.

One deck down, Com and Audrie paused at the entrance doors. The gigantic first class dining saloon was already half full. The hum of conversation dropped for a second as faces turned to look at them, then resumed. A dozen huge square columns covered with painted figures supported a ceiling decorated with coats of arms and panels of carved maritime scenes. Several vast, slow-moving fans turned through the air, while white-coated stewards stepped carefully between tables, carrying trays of food or bottles of wine. Ornately carved dark wooden chairs surrounded each table, each of which was fully laid in formal style.

Audrie dug the blue seating card out of her bag. 'We're at table 33. We should have asked to sit with some Ceylon people,' she muttered in trepidation, as they negotiated their way between the other diners towards their allotted table. Three of their dining companions for that evening were already seated. The table was hosted by a familiar-looking young assistant purser who looked, in his uncomfortably stiff uniform, ready to burst.

'Mr and Mrs Sutherland?' Their host introduced himself. 'I'm Gilbert, one of the assistant pursers. Welcome.'

'I believe we've met before.' Audrie looked at him. She remembered his stammer, his difficulty getting words out until he was comfortable in your company. 'Two years ago, coming out. I was Finch Noyes then.'

'My oh my, yes, I certainly remember you. With Mrs Mann?

You disembarked at Colombo.' They took their seats and once again they started to conduct that familiar slow verbal fencing and gradual exchange of information.

'These young ladies are travelling together,' Gilbert announced. 'Judith Seppelt and Angela Penfold.' One in blue, tall and fair, the other red-headed with a dramatic green brooch on her dress. They smiled up at Com and Audrie.

'You're going home on leave?' asked Miss Penfold.

'Yes, we are. First one since we were married,' said Com, 'and it's obvious, if I may say, where you two come from.'

'Australian accents are never difficult to spot,' said Miss Seppelt.

'Well, yes,' he went on, 'but I'm in the wine trade so I knew your family names immediately.'

'Oh, that,' grinned the second girl. 'People always think we should be enemies, coming from rival wine families, but we were at school at Frensham together, and now we're off to spend a year in Europe.'

Within a few minutes, the table company included an artillery major and his younger wife, also going home on leave, and the last to appear was a striking-looking dark-haired woman, very self-assured, well-dressed, ten years older than Audrie. She introduced herself as Zella Ratcliffe, who had joined ship at Fremantle. Audrie watched the newcomer, who was clearly quite used to handling herself when meeting a bunch of new people.

'I'm heading back to England to visit my late husband's family,' she told the company, as she settled in and the steward handed round the dinner menus. 'He was an engineer. We originally met and married in London, then went back to Australia for his work. But Roger died in a mining accident two years ago, just after my Peter was born, and his family have never met their grandson. I've asked the nursery stewardess to teach him how to speak like a true Brit.'

Mrs Ratcliffe's easy-going manner having broken the ice, conversation round the table became fluid, and Audrie started to relax.

'You're originally from Sydney, Mrs Ratcliffe?' Judith asked. 'Did you go to Frensham, too?'

'Hardly,' she grinned. 'My education was at Romano's Restaurant and The Embassy Club.' Audrie felt the tension go out of her back, everyone was smiling now, as the steward returned to take their orders.

'I'll have the Velouté Portugaise and the Farcied Cushion of Veal, please. Small portions.' She turned to Com. 'If they mean stuffed why don't they say so?'

'Stuffed? Because it's French food. Or at least, Orient Line food with French names. Makes a change from curry and rice.'

Compared to that last voyage, travelling home and back on her own after their engagement, to be with Com now was bliss, and she felt herself leaning back, as the assistant purser and Mrs Ratcliffe entertained the table with their stories of previous voyages.

'Coming up from Fremantle to Colombo,' Gilbert recalled, 'the ship ran into bad weather and started moving about a bit. Under these conditions the stewards often dampen the tablecloths to prevent the plates sliding about. One young lady at my table remarked that the tablecloth was wet. I told her, we always wet the table in rough weather. Stops things falling off, you know.'

"What a wonderful idea," the girl answered. "I think I'll wet my bed tonight."' He beamed around at everyone. There was a larger than usual lurch as *Orontes* plunged into a longer swell, and everyone picked up their glasses to stop the wine swilling about.

'You never know what you're going to hear on board ship,' Zella Ratcliffe recounted. 'One evening, on our last trip, we were taking a stroll, and just as we passed the doorway to the bridge, there was an American woman, dripping with jewels, holding a large martini, must have been her fourth or fifth. She was grasping the captain's arm, and she said, "Captain, how much longer do we have to endure the Red Sea and all this heat?" "Just for tonight, madam," replied the officer. "I'm advancing the ship's clocks a whole hour, so we'll be out of it sooner." "Really," she answered, "you sailors are so thoughtful."'

Com turned to grin at Audrie, who smiled and nodded. She was sure her father had told her the same one. Watching Com, she took a sip of wine and thought about coming home, and what her father would think when he finally got to know him. She had written to him to say how kind, gentle and considerate her husband was, and how hard he worked, but one could never tell if people were going to, well, just get on.

As the courses arrived, they found some of Angela's family's products on the *Orontes* wine list, and ordered two different whites with the fish and a Penfold red for later.

'Once it gets cooler we'll organise a sports committee; would anyone like to join?' asked Gilbert, as they were finishing dinner. 'What about you young ladies?'

'I'm game,' said Judith Seppelt. She looked to Audrie to be a sporty type.

'Me too,' echoed her school friend. 'What do we have to do?' Gilbert looked round the table.

'Well, we all meet, we appoint a secretary,' he explained, 'and we organise a series of events and amusements for the rest of the voyage. For example, did you know that *Orontes* was the first ship to have a full-size tennis court on deck? We could have a deck tennis tournament.'

'Tennis, yes, I'd love to play,' said Judith. 'But don't the balls go overboard all the time?'

'Well, it's not exactly like Wimbledon,' Gilbert smiled. 'We use rackets made of solid wood, but otherwise it's the same. We have shuffles, you know, deck quoits, or bull board.'

'Gilbert, yes,' said Audrie, 'I'd love to help out. Mrs Ratcliffe, will you join in?'

'Of course, why not? These passages can get very boring if there's nothing to do but read, eat and sleep.'

Having secured the first four members for his Sport and Entertainment Committee, the assistant purser excused himself after dinner, and returned to his duties, while Com and Audrie and their party moved into the smoking room for coffee. Half an hour later, having declined to join a four for bridge, she yawned and turned to her husband.

'Come on, then, let's take a turn around the deck before we collect Robin, and then bed.'

They excused themselves, leaving the major to continue his story, and they strolled out onto the deck arm in arm. It was not so hot now, and a soft wind blew across the ship from the south-west, catching the smoke from the funnels and blowing away to their right.

'Let's go forward,' she suggested, 'it's my favourite place. Is it out of bounds?'

'Probably. I'm not sure. Come on.'

They strolled on to the forward end of the promenade deck, and leaned out to gaze down, over the foremasts and anchor mechanism, towards the great bow of the ship as she ploughed through the Indian Ocean, churning a rolling wave up and out to each side. Out on the dark sea, thousands of luminescent flecks gleamed on the surface, as though *Orontes* was passing through a lake of silver and gold pieces. Gradually, a mile or two ahead and far off the starboard bow, they saw another ship, a big freighter, coming towards them with its deck lights gleaming – but going where? Audrie wondered, Ceylon? Or... some magical place, Java, the Spice Islands, the coast of Coromandel? The sight was impossibly romantic, and they watched in awe as the other great ship sped silently past.

Com shared her mood. '*Stately Spanish galleon coming from the Isthmus, Dipping through the Tropics by the palm-green shores,*' he quoted, as the other vessel vanished behind them. 'Below, the ship's company, hundreds of people all together. Then when you come out on deck, there's just the power of the engines underneath us, and the sea. It's so vast, so empty. It gives you a sense of such space, and such isolation, and makes problems and worries all seem so irrelevant.' He put his arm round her, as they stood, mesmerised by the flickering lights of the sea.

'I know, the same for me,' she answered. 'Each time I've been on passage out or home, I come up here and it seems that I'm apart from the whole world, almost on a different planet. Last time when I was coming back out, I spent half an hour up here one evening, thinking about us and what it would be like to be married to you.'

'And?'

'And... I decided I'd made a terrible mistake, it would be ghastly, unspeakably appalling and I'd give you back your ring.'

Com's face started to fall but then he saw her impish grin. 'Oh, well,' he countered, 'if that's the case I'll jump overboard at the next corner.'

'If you do, I'll throw you an anchor to keep you afloat. But now it's so wonderful,' she went on. 'That last time going back without you was awful. Never again.'

A mist of light spray caught them both in the face. Audrie turned towards Com, wiped his forehead with her fingertips, and stood on tiptoe to kiss him softly. 'Never again, d'you hear? I won't allow it. And this is going to be a wonderful home leave. You'll be able to relax at last.'

They turned back towards the door, down one flight of stairs and along to the night nursery, where the duty nursery stewardess was reading a book as she sat with Robin and one other little baby, each in cribs shaped like wooden boats with '*Orontes*' lettered on the side.

'He's been a little angel,' she said. 'Good as gold.'

'Thank you so much, good night.' Com picked up their son, who slept blissfully on as they returned to their cabin.

———————

'So, ladies and gentlemen, are we all agreed?' asked Gilbert, picking up his notebook. 'This Saturday evening, the *Orontes* Red Sea Race Meeting? Five races, followed by a final for the *Orontes* Cup.' The seven members of the new sports committee were gathered round a large window table in the B Deck first class lounge. The women were in summer dresses, some fanning themselves in the heat, while the assistant purser and the other men were in shirtsleeves.

'How many horses are there? How many owners and jockeys will we need?' Angela Penfold was an enthusiastic organiser. Audrie rather suspected she had used her new role to introduce herself to Adrian, the attractive young planter who sat opposite her.

'Well, we normally have five,' the assistant purser explained. 'Five horses in each race, that's twenty-five. Each one'll need to be nominated by someone who will pay their entry fee.'

'No trouble,' said Judith Seppelt, looking round the table at the other committee members. 'I'm sure Angela and Audrie and I can each rope in five or six other teams.'

Fine by me too,' Audrie nodded. She was enjoying this. The first time, travelling out, Peggy had managed to persuade her to go in for the race, but with Com at her side it was so much easier to meet new people.

'What about you, Mrs Ratcliffe?' Judith asked.

'Do call me Zella,' she replied, looking up from tatting a white collar. 'I can certainly try, there's a couple in the cabin next to me who are always talking about betting on this and that. And I'm sure some of the poker players in the smoke room would like to have a horse in a race.' She picked up her magnifying glass and examined the stitch. 'Drat, dropped it.'

'Bets are all on the Tote,' Gilbert went on. 'One shilling each horse, or two shillings for the double on the third and fifth race. The Tote pay-out depends on the number of bets. So, please be sure to let me have the names of owners and jockeys you've rounded up by five tomorrow, and I'll have the cards printed up for Friday.'

'Righto,' said Judith. 'We'll do our best.'

'Good luck,' Gilbert said, 'and look out for ladies with strong arms. That's the way to spot a winner.' He stood up, caught himself as the ship rose in a long swell, and set out for his office, while the remaining committee members gathered up their notes, finished their drinks and parted company.

'Darling, I've put your name down for the Red Sea Race Meeting,' Audrie announced as she returned to their cabin from the committee meeting. 'You're the owner of a horse in the second race, named Faux Pas. I'm the jockey. And you owe me two and six entry fee. Come on, get your hat on, we're going for a walk. Eight times round the Prom deck is a mile, so we have to do at least sixteen turns. And I've put us down for the shore party in Aden. We'll be there tomorrow.'

Com got up from the lounge chair and followed her out and up to the deck.

'How was your visit to Aden?' asked their new friend David McDonough, the artillery major, two days later. 'I was nearly posted there.'

Six hours after *Orontes* had sailed from the new colony, they were having coffee in the B Deck Café, looking out to starboard as the ship turned gradually around the corner past Perim Island, into the Mandeb Strait and the Red Sea. A graceful dhow, with its sail just filling in the calmer air, lay a few hundred yards towards the shoreline, with a range of low, brown mountains in the distance.

'Hated it,' Audrie replied. 'Lucky man to avoid it. Incredibly hot. It's desolate, simply bare rock and no vegetation whatsoever. We were told that the last rainfall was over two years ago. The streets were filthy, dusty and full of goats. The poverty is much worse than Colombo. We were accosted by beggars the moment we stepped on shore. And as soon as Com gave one of them, it was a blind man, some coins, the others got worse and we were followed by half a dozen others for ten minutes.'

Com picked up the story. 'And later, as we were returning after a dismal lunch at the Empire Restaurant, there was the "blind" beggar sitting in the dust outside a shop, counting his money. Anyway, are you two in the Race Meeting this evening?'

'We certainly are,' confirmed Mary McDonough. 'Have you done it before?'

'I certainly have, twice,' Audrie echoed, sipping her coffee. 'First, coming out in January thirty-seven and again, when I was put up for it by a sweet man I met on my last trip out, before we were married.'

'You never told me about him,' Com laughed. 'You told me you hadn't even used the pink ticket.'

'Stop it… it was perfectly all right; he was married, but his wife was pregnant and couldn't be a jockey, so I volunteered.'

'What exactly does happen?' asked Mary. 'David's signed me in for it; what do I have to do?'

'It's up on top, on A Deck,' Audrie explained. 'The jockeys are all women. You have a reel, like a fishing rod only bigger, with twenty yards of line. The other end is fixed to the nose of your horse.' She held her hand out at knee height. 'Its legs are on a wooden stand. You have to reel it in along the track, from the start to the finish.'

'Sounds easy enough.'

'It's much harder than it looks. Twenty yards of cord take a lot of reeling in and you need a strong arm. Last time I was very stiff afterwards. And it's impossible to keep it in a straight line so you get entangled with the others. And on top of that, everyone's jostling you and shouting and cheering.'

Com waved at the steward. 'Talking of stiff arms, let's order a drink.'

'Good idea,' said David, looking over Com's shoulder. They all became aware of a general stirring in the room, as a group sitting at a table across the café by the port window stood up, and others followed suit. 'But hello,' he went on, 'look, another ship. It's a big one. Let's go out and see.'

Through the far windows of the café, they could all now see a large liner bearing down on them. There was a general hubbub as everyone in the café pushed back their chairs, Com and their companions followed the crowd as they hurried out on deck. One of *Orontes'* sister ships, *Orion*, was steaming near them on the opposite route, on passage to Australia. The latest addition to the Orient Line fleet, *Orion* was larger and faster than *Orontes*, and so the ships passed each other at a combined speed of more than 30 knots. As the group came out on deck to watch her go by, a hundred yards away, they saw outgoing passengers were doing the same thing. Dozens had come out on deck to wave their handkerchiefs to *Orontes* as the sister ships passed.

'There's something wonderful about seeing a great ship going at full speed, close up,' Com observed. 'At Aden, she'll be picking up the mails for Colombo. Your postcard from Aden will be with Kay by Wednesday.' They watched her out of sight as she raced on down to the strait.

That evening as *Orontes* continued up towards Suez, the moon was out, the following wind had died down, and the seas were glassy calm after the long swells of the Indian Ocean. After dinner, their party joined more than a hundred and fifty other passengers gathered on the open boat deck to enjoy the *Orontes* Red Sea Race Meeting.

Gilbert's official race card now included five races, The Fremantle Frolic, The Colombo Canter, The Aden Amble, The Suez Stakes and The Tilbury Trot, followed by the final for the Cup.

At nine pm, the ladies of the first race were lined up and ready to start winding. As the stewards finished setting up, the racegoers crowded round the track to watch the action. The Tote was doing good business under the awning, with a strong-looking blonde woman the probable favourite in the first.

The first race was a disaster. Colonel Parsons had put 'Bloodstock breeder' as his occupation, which should have qualified him. But he didn't understand deck racing, and couldn't hear Gilbert's instructions very well. He was supposed to hold up a flag to mark Starters Orders, but blew the 'GO!' whistle first. Confusion erupted, strings were wound, elbows flailed.

'Halt! As you were!' Parsons ordered, when he realised what he'd done. The crowd laughed, the jockeys disentangled themselves and unwound their cords, while stewards pulled the horses back to the line and prepared them to restart. Gilbert, accompanied by a waiter bearing a tray with a large whisky, approached and whispered a few words in the colonel's ear. The old boy beamed, took the whisky, agreed to sit the card out, and handed over his flag and whistle. He received a round of applause for his efforts, as the head purser took over. From then on, it was calmer, for the starts at least.

Angela and Judith both won their heats. The finalists were called to their positions for the *Orontes* Cup and their horses' strings were drawn back taut to the start line. The five women lined up. Two of them had shed their deck shoes and now stood barefoot, holding their reel forward and with their knees bent in a classic starting position, as though set to run the hundred yards. The chief purser raised his flag. The whistle blew and they were away. Five determined jockeys furiously wound their reels in as their wooden horses slid across the track towards them. The volume increased as the race got to the halfway mark and it was Angela who fairly whizzed her horse up to the finish line to take the cup.

Captain Baillie, as president of the Race Meeting, now appeared to present Angela with the trophy, and her prize money, to general cheers from the crowd. A few minutes later, now with her shoes back on, she rejoined the party, flushed with success, panting a little, and with her planter friend Adrian on her arm.

'What a great girl,' he said proudly. 'She won three pounds twelve. And did you see the Tote pay-out? I had ten bob on her in the fourth, and another ten in the final, and it's netted me four pounds – come on – we're all off to the bar for champagne.'

As *Orontes* headed north up the Gulf towards Suez, the next day brought a post-race hangover for the Sutherlands and their friends, and in the heat of the Gulf, nobody felt much like doing anything.

On her way past the giant complex of oil wells at Ras Gharib, the ship crossed several others heading south, before entering the Gulf of Suez a day later at Shadwan Island. But when she finally arrived at Suez itself, *Orontes* waited outside the harbour, with her anchor dropped, before starting up the first part of the canal to the Bitter Lake. Pilot boats delivered port officers to examine the ship's papers before entering the Canal, while Captain Baillie spent a quarter of an hour on the R/T to his colleague at the Suez harbour master's office, trying to arrange for his ship, as an official Royal Mail Steamer, to jump the queue.

Finally they were under way and *Orontes* edged into the canal. Audrie, on her fourth trip through in two years, felt quite like an old hand, so declined to join the Australian girls to watch the camels walking along beside the ship. Instead, she and Com sat down to play bridge in the first class smoking room, with the McDonoughs making up a four, and the baby sleeping happily beside them.

For the most part, between bids, everyone talked about the heat. One of the ship's cooks had suffered heatstroke and had to be put ashore at Suez to be taken to hospital, while many of the third class passengers, normally sharing a lower deck cabin for six without a porthole, had been given permission to come up and sleep in the open air.

As soon as they arrived at the other end of the Canal, at Port Said, the ship was surrounded by dozens of bumboats, each with their traders calling up to offer their goods.

Three days and twelve hundred nautical miles later, *Orontes* docked alongside in Naples, where she was due to remain for twelve hours. Immediately she was tied up fore and aft, and the long white gangways in place, black-shirted customs officers and port officials marched officiously onto the ship to inspect her papers. Gilbert stood at the rail to hand out shore passes. Audrie and Com, setting out to go ashore, came across the two young Australian women at the top of the gangway.

'Good morning, girls,' Audrie called. 'Where are you off to this morning?'

'G'day, Aud, Com.' Judith smiled at them, brandishing her map. 'We're going to Tekator. Back for lunch.'

'How lovely,' Audrie responded, without a clue where that was. 'And what plans do you have for this afternoon?'

'After lunch?' Angela responded. 'Take another tour.'

The *Orontes* visitors leaflet for Naples recommended a restaurant on the hill towards the Castel Sant'Elmo, with a wide terrace giving a spectacular view of the bay. On arrival, the view was everything the brochure suggested, and they enjoyed their first-ever Neapolitan pasta and seafood, with the waiters flirting with Audrie – *che bella signora* – and dancing attendance on the baby.

They were back at the quayside an hour and a half before the five o'clock departure, and having handed in their shore passes and climbed back aboard, they paused on C Deck, near the gap in the rail, to watch a huge mass of local people crowding around the forward third class gangway below. Several large Neapolitan family groups had come to bid *Buon viaggio* to their relations, who, Audrie thought, judging from the amount of luggage, must be setting out for work or for a new life in Britain.

At a signal from the uniformed *Orontes* crewman on the pier, the crowd surged forward to collect their onboard farewell passes, and start mounting the steep gangway. In some strange Italian way, the crowd seemed to become a single file on the stair without any actual queuing taking place. A mass of humanity went to and fro as whole families hurried up on board with their departing family member, to see them off properly and, of course, to take a look around the ship.

As Com and Audrie watched, one very large woman, labouring slowly up in the middle of the busy gangway, seemed to change her mind. She turned, waved frantically, grabbed the handrail, and called back to someone on the quayside. Then, lifting up the little girl by her side, she started to push her way back down. A logjam built up and stopped in front of her. At that moment, a bugle blew to warn all visitors on board to go ashore, and then a voice announced in English that *Orontes* would sail in fifteen minutes. Confusion ensued, as some had understood and some clearly hadn't. The *Orontes* quartermaster at the foot of the stair blew his whistle and signalled for guests to start back down to the quay. People from the deck turned to go back, others swarmed round the lower part, but there were others, new, late arrivals who now started trying to mount the gangway.

Something was going wrong. Audrie gripped Com's arm. Along the decks above them, other passengers were watching the scene unfold. It happened very suddenly.

Someone tripped over and two others lurched dangerously near the rail. There was a loud cracking sound and the long gangplank started to give way at the centre. People fell and started to slide back towards the quay as the centre of the structure groaned and then snapped. At the top end people frantically grabbed the handrail and jumped back on board, or hung there pleading for help. The two sailors at the shipboard gangway entrance were leaning over to help people climb back up and onto the ship. Audrie and Com leaned further forward to see what was happening just below, Audrie's hand flying to her mouth as she gave an involuntary shriek as she saw the full scene developing.

Several men and women, one with a small child, shouted for help as they slid or dropped into the narrow space of water between the ship and the quay. The quartermaster blew his whistle constantly and signalled to force onlookers back from the concrete wharf. Sailors and dockworkers ran towards the edge and threw lifebelts and long ropes at the struggling swimmers. Most had reached a rope or a lifebuoy. But the big woman with the little girl was already in trouble. Her wide skirt had spread out on the surface and she was flapping her hands wildly to keep afloat, while reaching out for her daughter. For a moment the little girl's dark head appeared but then vanished again in the dirty water. Audrie couldn't help screaming with alarm as she saw the danger.

Com handed his jacket to his wife, ran along the deck to the edge of the gangway and jumped over into the water. After the splash, he reappeared nearer the flailing woman and with a few strong strokes he was next to her. Kicking out to tread water, he put his hands up in the air to show her he was ready to help, and his head then vanished under the water as he grabbed for the little girl. Simultaneously there was another splash and the head of a young *Orontes* crewman appeared next to them, with a lifebuoy ring for the woman.

On the pier, a bearded man in a blue uniform was shouting down to the swimmers. He gestured and pointed along the quay, and Com, his eyes smarting from the filthy water, but now holding the girl, could just about see a set of steps set in the side of the wall by the bow of the ship, thirty yards away. He set out, swimming on his back and holding the little girl, who was constantly thrashing and screaming, towards the stair. As Com swam up, a seaman ran down and knelt down to reach for the girl, wrapping her in a big coat and handing her to a colleague while he helped Com pull himself out of the water. He clambered out of the way as another dock worker arrived at the bottom of the steps, pulling in the rope attached to the lifebuoy ring, with the mother clinging on and still screaming.

Up above, Audrie handed Robin to Judith, ran down the forward stairs to the quay and pushed her way through the crowd. Com, now surrounded by clamouring Italians, was standing in his dripping shirt and flannels. Beside him, mother and daughter, soaked but apparently none the worse for wear, were being comforted by others of their family.

'My darling wet hero husband. Are you all right?'

'That water is absolutely filthy,' Com announced, in his best matter-of-fact voice. 'These trousers are ruined. I think there's a crab in my pocket. I need a large whisky to take the taste away, and a hot bath.'

As Audrie led him back up on board, people slapped him on the back and shook his hand, the British muttering 'Good Show' while the Italians, more exuberant, clapped and cheered *Bravo, Bravissimo, Magnifico, Bellissimo.*

Once the remains of the broken gangway had been removed, statements had been given to the port police, and every legitimate passenger safely re-boarded, *Orontes* left Naples two hours late. That evening, as they were preparing to go to dinner, there was a knock on their stateroom door, and a steward delivered a note from Captain Baillie. Com and Audrie were invited to join him in his cabin for a pre-dinner drink, and later to dine at his table.

The steward escorted them to A Deck, where on arrival at the captain's quarters, they found other guests already there. Captain Baillie welcomed Com and Audrie and introduced them first to Signor Cassandro, the father of the little girl whom Com had helped rescue, then to her mother, to the smiling young seaman who had leaped to help Signora Cassandro, and finally to another Italian passenger who interpreted for them.

Captain Baillie had, he said, been delighted to arrange for Mr Cassandro to meet and thank the English gentlemen who had saved the lives of his wife and daughter. The Italians had never before tasted Orient Line Gin, and the large measures handed round by the captain's steward greatly encouraged the ensuing back-slapping, kissing and smiling, while the interpreter struggled to give an adequate English version of Mr Cassandro's tearful speech. Audrie wished she could speak Italian to tell the mother how shocked she'd been and how pleased that Com had been there to help them.

On 25 April, after an uneventful trip through the Straits of Gibraltar and across the Bay of Biscay, *Orontes* deposited its passengers at Tilbury. Fond farewells took place with Judith and Angela, Zella

Ratcliffe and the McDonoughs, before the Sutherlands took the boat train to Fenchurch Street.

Finch, Joy and Audrie's sister, Chim, were waiting at the barrier, and as she caught sight of them, dressed in heavy dark clothing against the cold wind, Audrie found herself crying with happiness. Brushing away her tears, she handed the baby to Com, ran forward to hug and kiss her parents and her sister, and then introduce her husband and baby. Com proudly handed Robin over to his beaming grandmother, then it was Chim's turn. Audrie took her father's arm, and they set off, shivering, towards a waiting taxi, and a celebration dinner at the Oriental Club.

After a night in London, the family took the train for the Finch Noyes' home in Sussex, to enjoy some peace and quiet in the first months of their long-awaited home leave.

Aberdeen, 3rd September 1939

'Dad, it's ten past.' Com replaced the telephone receiver in the hall and called up to the landing. 'Come on down as soon as you can. Chamberlain's on in a few minutes. The whole country'll be listening. And my brother says he'll come over at lunchtime.'

Outside, it was a wet and gusty September day, with a cold wind blowing in across Aberdeen from the North Sea. The maid had lit the fire in the sitting room where Audrie, with the baby on her arm, was gazing in incomprehension at the wireless. 'How does this thing work? I can't understand it, I switched it on and nothing happens.'

'Is it warmed up? The valves have to warm up,' Com suggested. 'I'll draw the curtains.' As he pulled the heavily lined curtains across, he noted the couple opposite running to their front door in the rain.

His parents' sitting room was arranged round the open fireplace, beside which a large brown and cream wireless set stood out as the only brightly coloured item among dark wood bookcases, chintz-covered chairs and a comfortable-looking sofa.

'Here, stay with him,' Com told her, 'and I'll tune it in. Mugs is on her way.' Audrie laid the baby on the sofa, then sat beside him and propped him up with a cushion so he couldn't roll away from her. She could hear her in-laws muttering as they descended the stairs.

'It'll be bad news, I'll be bound.' The door pushed open and Com's father, also named Robert, helped his wife Mary move her stick from one hand to the other as she negotiated the way to her chair by the fire. Com found the BBC Home Service.

'Dad, Mugs, a drink? Tea?'

'I'll wait till later, thank you.' They fussed about, and were all seated by the time the announcer came on.

'This is London. You will now hear a statement from the Prime Minister.'

Com and Audrie exchanged a glance, and she closed her eyes in silent prayer. When he spoke, Neville Chamberlain's voice was thin, weary and disillusioned. Britain was at war with Germany. After the PM's broadcast, the BBC announced a series of air raid precautions.

'They say they will be bombing all the ports,' Mary Sutherland moaned, 'and that means us. It was like that last time with the Zeppelins.'

'Nonsense, woman,' her husband reassured her. 'Hitler has nothing against you, and there's no sense in bombing the fish.'

'She'll be fine.' He dismissed his wife's fears with a wave of his hand. 'But I will have that drink after all.' He made his way briskly over to the sideboard, opened a cupboard and pulled out a bottle of Stand Fast. 'And, Bobby, will you not join me?' He held up the bottle and a soda siphon. 'What will you do now?'

'A bit early for me,' Com smiled. 'Father, I've thought about this almost every day since Munich. Anybody could see another war was coming, but of course I'd no idea it would happen while we're here at home.' He looked across at Audrie as he went on, 'If you don't mind, can we stay on here a while longer, and next week, I'll apply to join the Gordons, I'm sure they need everyone they can get.'

Audrie stared blankly at her husband. 'What are the Gordons? What on earth do you mean?'

'Gordon Highlanders. It's the local regiment. At school we all joined the OTC. And you know, in Calcutta I was a lieutenant in the Cal and Pres.'

'Surely you don't have to join up,' she pleaded. 'You're too important. There are much younger men. And of course we must get back, you have your duty in Colombo, not here.'

Com had been eleven when the first war came, and like any other Aberdeen lad had been filled with patriotic determination to grow up in time to take part. Now, he knew, all his contemporaries would be joining up, and he must do so too.

'Of course I must go, everyone will have to. I'll go and see Jimmy Gardner.'

Three days later, Com borrowed his father's car and drove in steady rain, from Salisbury Terrace, out through the city for a few miles north, to Bridge of Don, At the barracks gate, shining with newly installed barbed wire, the sentry checked a list inside his hut, raised the barrier, and directed Com to the admin block a hundred yards away, where he parked the Austin and ran into the building with his coat over his head.

The duty sergeant led him through the open office, past half a dozen clerks who looked up from their work to gaze at the civilian outsider, and up to a door marked *Adjutant*. He knocked and then stood back to allow Com to pass.

'Sir. Mr Sutherland, sir.'

'Come in! My Lord, Bobby Sutherland in person, it's a wee while since we've seen your ugly face around these parts.'

Major Jimmy Gardner of the Gordon Highlanders pushed his chair back and strode round the desk to pump Com's hand, punching his arm with the other fist. 'How long has it been? What brings you back to Aberdeen? Here, let me take that, sit down here, come near the fire. Not that it's any use, just one bar.'

'Hello, Jimmy, very good to be back. You're looking very well.' Com handed over his wet coat and stood for while looking at his school friend. Com's tweed jacket, his only warm one, was a legacy from university days, and looked distinctly shabby next to Jimmy's impeccable uniform.

'I'm delighted to see you – but you're the last person I expected.'

'I was back on long home leave when the balloon went up. I see you're a major now; many congratulations.'

Gardner touched the crown on his shoulder. 'I've twelve years of service now, and this, well, it comes with the job.'

'Very impressive. And thanks for seeing me at such short notice.'

'We've as much time as we need, I'm not passing up a chance to catch up with an old chum, even if there's a war on. Cigarette? No? How've you been, I hear you're the big boss in Colombo now, selling more whisky than they can make.'

'So my brother's been talking…?' Com's started to speak but his reply was drowned by a drill squad on the parade ground.

'New recruits, all joined last week. So, how long is it, eight years?'

'I went out in twenty-six, the same year that you joined this bunch, and my first home leave was in thirty-one, so nine years since then. We delayed my last break so as to make arrangements for the wedding, and then the baby…'

'I heard you were a married man. For how long are you home?'

'That's what I wanted to talk about. How long we stay, I mean. I'm going to join up, and naturally it'd be the Gordons, so I thought of you.'

'Join us? Good idea. Have you done any soldiering since the OTC at school?'

'The OTC only started the year before I left,' Com said. 'But since then, all the usual stuff. Five years with the Calcutta and Presidency Battalion in Madras, second lieutenant, you know the thing, an auxiliary force, they say it's a volunteer regiment but you have to do it or they treat you like an outcast. Then when Cutler's transferred me down to run the Colombo operation, I joined the CPRC, the Planters' Rifles, a good bunch, all British expatriates. They call it planters, but most of them are office wallahs, never seen a tea garden. There, you're just a private, but we'll be sent off for officer training in due course.'

Gardner was silent for a while, and then walked over to a large cabinet, extracting a brown file. 'How's your health?'

'Fine, all well, everything works, a bit of asthma brought on by life in the tropics, but otherwise no damage.'

'And if you joined us, you'd have to do basic training as a private, before applying for a commission, is that understood? It's the same for everyone now.'

'Aye, of course.' Gardner's Aberdeen accent sounded so comforting that Com dropped easily back into the language of his childhood.

'But with your experience, and a brain like yours,' Gardner went on, 'I'm sure I could see to it that you were selected for officer training pretty quickly.'

'You are? That'd be grand.' The squad outside were at the far end of the parade ground and the sergeant's yells were less obtrusive.

The adjutant opened a drawer and handed a sheaf of papers to Com. 'Fill in these recruitment forms and drop them off with the sergeant in the main building. He'll give you an appointment for an interview and a medical in a day or so. Come back here in an hour and let's go and have some lunch. Are you still playing chess?'

'Will do. Yes, as much as I can, it whiles away the long evenings when Audrie and I are apart. Jimmy, I can't thank you enough.'

'Nothing to it. We need men like you.'

Com was shown into a roomful of waiting recruits. He spent the next half an hour filling in the forms; giving his parents' address, answering questions about his age, education and experience, his health, his family situation, single, married, children, ages of children. Under Sports, he wrote 'Rowing, tennis, golf, swimming', and in the section *Other Hobbies and Interests*, he put 'Chess, mathematical puzzles and crosswords'.

Com handed the papers in to the sergeant, and was given an appointment to come for the interview and medical two days later. Once again, he pondered what he'd say to his family.

'When would you have to join?' asked Audrie. They stood a little way apart, in the kitchen at Salisbury Terrace, drinking cups of tea and staring out at the little back garden and the terrace of houses behind. Robin, recently fed, was dozing in his mother's arms. 'And when you do, where would we go, the baby and I? Back to Mum and Dad in Sussex? Or back to Colombo? Stay here? How will we manage?'

'We'll have to think about it. It's the same for everyone, nobody can tell what will happen. I'm certainly not going to leave you two here if there are going to be air raids.' He finished his cup and ran it under the tap.

'Never mind the air raids,' Audrie pleaded. 'Couldn't we just go home first, close everything up and then come back? We've enough saved for the passage. I could do it, on my own, but what about him' – she rocked the baby in her arms – 'and of course what about Cutler's?'

'Darling, you know if they say yes, it'll be start now, right away,' Com replied. 'I've asked Jimmy for a favour, to push me up the list, not down it. I can't back down and say "Please, sir, may I join up in six months' time?" You can't keep the army waiting.'

'But if they take you straight away, what would we do?'

'I'll telegraph the old man in the morning, and give him my notice,' Com said, 'He won't be pleased but he'll have to understand. He'll have to promote David Peacock if he hasn't already joined up.'

'You could stay here, I suppose,' he continued, thinking aloud, 'and I'd get occasional leave, but we would hardly see each other. Mugs would fuss and fret all the time and you know what a bad heart she has. But could you telephone your father and see what he proposes? You could stay a while with them in Sussex. But if they take me, I'm afraid you'll have to go back to Colombo at some stage, and close everything up.' Com was trying to keep a calm face while he thought desperately how to avoid Audrie having to do all this on her own.

'So...' She too was keeping her voice low while she felt a mounting sense of panic. 'So let's see what happens when you go back for the interviews, and meanwhile, we'll keep our options open.' They washed up the tea things and went back into the drawing room where Robert was reading the *Press and Journal* while Mugs dozed quietly in her chair.

The next morning, Com drove down to the post office and telegraphed the chairman of Cutler's in Colombo, to give notice that he must resign to join up.

Two days later, Com took a bus to the Gordons' barracks at Bridge of Don for his appointment. When his name was finally called, the interview was perfunctory and, he wrote later, easy enough. Thousands of men had joined up since the outbreak of war, and the pressure was on to get things moving. Of course he had left his Calcutta and Presidency Battalion service record back in Colombo, but the panel was satisfied with his forms. They asked a few more questions about his work and interests, and quickly passed him on to the medical examiner.

When the telephone in the hallway rang a few days later, his father answered and then handed Com the receiver. 'Major Gardner calling, for you. Would that be young Jimmy?' Com nodded to his father, who left him alone in the hallway and returned to the sitting room.

'Jimmy, old man. Good to hear from you.'

'Com, yes, it's me. But you won't be too happy. It's bad news I'm afraid. The board've turned you down.'

'Down? What on earth do you mean? I thought they wanted everyone they can get? Surely it's just a formality?'

'Well, it's nothing seriously wrong. There are a number of things, but for a start, you're too old.'

'Too old? I don't believe it.'

'You're not by any means a priority, not what we're looking for right now. I'm told the policy is to take fit men aged 18 to 25, and give priority to bachelors. And of course you're thirty-seven, married and with a baby.'

'Lord Almighty, Jimmy, that's not what I expected.'

'There's more, I'm sorry to say, the MO's report. They were worried about your sinus and the asthma. It occurred to me when you told me, but I wanted to wait for the official verdict. That's an immediate no for a line regiment. They can't be stopping the attack while you take your asthma pill. I'm sorry to be flip, but there it is.' Com shuddered at the feeling of rejection. He felt fitter than most men ten years younger. He breathed out and pushed his shoulders down.

'It's all right, Jimmy. I understand.' And then, half to himself, 'Too old. Married. A child. Asthma. Not wanted by King and Country.'

'Never mind, Com. Don't fret. Be patient. With your brains and training, there'll be something for you. Maybe intelligence? Hang on a week or two. I'll see what I can do.'

'Jimmy, old man, thank you so much for your help.' Com ran a pencil along the wooden rails of the staircase. 'But I can't just sit and wait. I've resigned my spot at Cutler's in Colombo. I'll telegraph again, but it may be too late, the old boy will have found someone else. I can't wait around to see what happens. I've got to get back.'

He put down the telephone, and as he sat down on the small chair beside the staircase, turned to find Audrie standing beside him, eyebrows raised.

'Was that what I thought it was?'

He nodded and stood up. 'Too old.'

'You poor boy.' She stepped closer, and put her arms around his neck and her face on his chest. 'But it means we three can be together.'

They remained silent for a minute. 'My darling. Well, at least we don't have to worry about what next.'

'No, thank God. Everything's easier when you can see clearly what you must do. We must go back.'

'I'll sail back as planned, stupid to waste the passage money. But I'll have to find a new job. I'll telegraph old Slater. He always says they'd be pleased to have me at the Colombo Apothecaries whenever I was ready for a change. Meanwhile, you and Robin can stay on with your family down in Sussex, and join me as soon as I've got everything arranged.' Audrie tried hard to smile and put on a brave face, but her chest felt very tense. 'It'll be very difficult to change our bookings. Let's go to the shipping agent tomorrow, there'll be all sorts of new priorities now there's a war on.'

At the end of their leave, Com hurried back to Ceylon, sailing from Tilbury on board RMS *Orcades*, to make sure he could start work promptly in the new post he'd been offered at the Colombo Apothecaries Company. Audrie returned to her parents in Sussex, and having waited for a while, due to new wartime movement restrictions, finally took passage in January 1940, on RMS *Orama*, bound for Ceylon and Australia via the Cape.

As soon as *Orama* had left the Solent, there was an announcement for an emergency boat drill, after which the entire ship's company were told there were U-boats operating in the South Atlantic. But, said the captain, 'Not to worry, they won't find us.'

Orama would travel alone, the passengers were told, and their main defence against attack was *Orama's* speed, more than 20 knots. Audrie had to quickly learn the emergency boat drill and how to find her way around the ship in the dark.

'They told us all to prepare a bag with some essential items,' she wrote, 'which we could get hold of quickly in case of an emergency. Thank God I did what he said as I'm sure it wouldn't have turned out as we did without the things I took.'

She followed all the safety guidelines. She took several walks, carrying Robin, between her cabin, four decks down, and the open deck, and also from the public rooms, so that she 'knew every straight, bend, corner and stairway in detail in case of an alarm.'

Most of the time, she'd sat out in the open, 'like so much deck cargo', playing with Robin, and taking it in turns with the other mothers to queue to get hot water to feed and change him, keeping her bag of precious things right next to her at all times. 'Every day there was another boat drill at ten o'clock, and then it happened.'

'I was rocking Robin in one arm, when there was a tremendous bang. Immediately the alarms started sounding, everyone to emergency stations. I ran outside onto the deck. To our horror there was another loud explosion, and the whole ship seemed to shudder and stop.'

There was tumult, everyone was shouting, Robin was crying and she tried to calm him and herself down. The crewmen kept reassuring them, she wrote, and she was astonished how everyone was so calm.

Everybody helped those with children to get into their allocated boat, and when Audrie's boat was full, with about seventy aboard, sailors began to lower it to the water. Seamen were also loading extra stores into the boats and the big launches. As soon as their boat touched the water, the crew started to pump the propeller so they could move away from the ship. The boat drifted slowly astern, while they waited to be taken in tow by the powered launches, five to one launch. In the rolling swell, and now exposed, Audrie felt slightly sick and wrapped herself and Robin in the blankets which were handed round.

The captain and some of the crew had stayed on board, as *Orama* wasn't sinking. They were trying to fix the steering, and then she would head very slowly to Cape Town for repairs. Their little convoy started out, and motored for about five hours, with the launches regularly sending up flares, until rescue came at about four in the afternoon.

'We were spotted and rescued by a steamer which had received the SOS and very bravely searched for us in spite of the risk of being attacked by the same U-boat.'

They all clambered up and on board. Audrie wrote, 'It was actually harder climbing up from the lifeboats than it had been getting in.' They were given hot drinks and milk for the little ones, and she was able to wash the baby and settle him down on a blanket.

Soon after their rescue, news came that *Orama* had been attacked once again and this time, been sunk, but that nearly everyone had been saved. The rescued passengers and crew arrived in Cape Town the following day, and thank to her emergency bag, Audrie had some money. She cabled Com with the news of her rescue, also telling him at the same time that they had been attacked.

'I told him all this,' she wrote to her mother, 'or at least the parts which will get past the censor. You can imagine how worried he had been when we sailed, but he'd never even heard that we had been attacked. I've told him we were safe and well, before he knew we hadn't been, if you see what I mean.' Finally, she asked them not to worry, and closed the letter with a prediction.

'We are indeed now safe, thank God, and I really do feel now that I've been in the war. It will be an adventure to tell the grandchildren.'

Laverstock, Bambalapitya, 30th January 1940

I've just received your cable and replied. God Almighty you poor darling. What a terrible experience for you both. It's such a relief to know you have finally arrived safely but I can't imagine what you went through. Impossible to think that you were going through all that while I was blithely ignorant of it all here. Cannot wait to hear what happened, I shall ask at Naval HQ if they have anything. Cable if you need money. With all my love, C

Once Com and Audrie had been safely reunited, life at Laverstock could return to normal, although having started his new post as MD of the Colombo Apothecaries, Ceylon's largest pharmaceutical concern, he found that the war at sea was already causing shortages of drugs and medical supplies.

As many younger Europeans were called up or returned to Britain to join the forces, another shortage – management talent – was emerging across the island's expatriate-owned businesses. Com was invited to take on another role as head of the Kandy Hotels Group, which meant a weekly four-hour train journey or drive up into the hills to supervise the Queen's and Hotel Suisse, favourites of travellers since Victorian times.

Soon after their return, an airmail letter arrived from Scotland. 'Darling, there's a letter from Aberdeen.' Audrie ran towards Com and anxiously held out the envelope to him. There was a white sticker on it, 'Opened by Censor.'

'It's from Jimmy Gardner of the Gordons.'

'Don't tell me. I can't bear it.' She closed her eyes. 'They're not going to take you away from me, are they?'

'Dear Com,' he read.

I hope you are all back safely in Colombo. I'm sorry to be the bearer of news you won't want to hear, but it seems there's little chance of your being able to join us in the Gordons, or any other regiment for the moment.

If you are in London, there are a couple of people I could fix for you to go and see. Meanwhile I've forwarded your details to ■■■■■■■■■■ [1], *remember him, anyway he's in Naval hush-hush now, told him about you and your readiness to help out there. All good wishes, I'll keep in touch and let you know. Jimmy*

Audrie opened her eyes and exhaled. 'Thank God for that.'

Tuesday 2nd May 1940
Dearest Mums & Dads
I hope you're all right. We listen to the news from home three times a day and cross our fingers. Things seem to be moving so fast you scarcely know what is happening.
Com needs a break. He's working twelve, fourteen, hours a day and, with this new job at the Kandy Hotels, sometimes all weekend, so I don't know how he stays awake. But we didn't go to Kandy last weekend as there have been terrific floods up-country, worse than anything for over 30 years. Kandy and the whole district from Hatton and Norwood to Nawalapitya and round the other way is completely cut off, railway bridges down, roads completely under water. There are floods in all the low-lying parts of Colombo by Victoria Bridge and all along the Kelani valley and at Galle and Inatara.
For the last 10 days or so it has been beautifully cool down here although I find my shoes and dresses get mould on them if I'm not careful. I shall have to get a bar for my cupboard, just as you predicted.
Love to you all from us three.

---

[1] Deleted by the censor

The Grand Oriental Hotel, commonly known as the GOH, was a large white landmark almost opposite the landing stage of Colombo port, in the busy Fort district, the financial and commercial centre of Colombo. On its wide facade, Ionic columns rose between the windows of the second and third floors, while contrasting bands of terracotta facings gave the building an odd, striped look. Com used it often for lunch, as it was near the main branch of the Colombo Apothecaries.

As her car approached the port entrance, Audrie could see tugs bustling around a huge grey warship at the entrance of the harbour. Outside the hotel, rickshaw coolies stripped to the waist, leaning on their vehicles, waited for trade. Their calls to departing guests mingled with the constant hooting of car horns and jingling bicycle bells.

Inside Audrie's heels clacked on the black and white-tiled floor as she crossed the hall towards the huge dining room, with its huge white pillars. The head waiter recognised her, and escorted her to a table by the harbour-side window where Kay Garland was waiting.

'According to Neil,' she chattered away, 'Michael's spending some time at the Lipton office down here, the usual estate admin, and then taking a few days off in town. Charlie asked if we'd look after him. It's apparently the first time he's come down to Colombo in ages. But you met him before, didn't you? Charlie said you bowled him over.'

Audrie peeled off her gloves. 'Bowled him over? Nonsense – we were fellow passengers on *Orontes* when I first came back out with Aunt Peggy.' Thinking about what had happened since then, 1937 seemed to be five life chapters ago. 'We danced one evening, that's all. He must have been here, more than three years now.'

'Nearly four,' Kay laughed. 'Up-country with Charlie and Anna he's had virtually no social life, hasn't seen another European woman for months, let alone any girlfriends. Wasn't allowed to come down for their wedding as it would have left the place deserted at a busy time.'

'So lunch with us two should be a great treat, I would say.' Audrie smiled.

'Anyway, even if we're old married ladies now, we're the nearest thing here to people of his own age.' She picked up a menu.

'Maybe we should introduce him to Laura?'

'She'd probably overwhelm him,' Kay laughed. 'Talks non-stop. A nightmare. Always asking what sex is like. Anyway she's only eighteen. You don't need to play cupid for my sister at that age…'

'You're right. From what we saw the other evening, she's doing rather well on her own.'

'Just what *did* you see?' asked Kay.

'Oh, we were at a party out at Mount Lavinia, she was flirting wildly with the Lushington boy. She may even have sat on his lap. He was very taken.'

'I can't wait to tease her about that,' Kay laughed. 'Anyway, what was it you wanted to tell me?'

Audrie took a deep breath. 'Kay, it's wonderful news and we wanted you and Neil to be the first to know.'

'Oh, don't tell me, how lovely, I can guess.'

'Yes, we're going to have another baby, it's due in July. I had a test three days ago and all is well.'

'My darling, so many congratulations.' Kay stood up and came round the table to kiss her. 'Let's order a proper drink.'

'We've decided if it's a girl, we'll call her Susan, and if a boy, then Alasdair. And Kay, thanks to you, I finally gave the cook his notice!' Audrie smiled in triumph. Since her return to Colombo, Audrie had always turned to her girlfriends with her household problems, and from the beginning, when they moved in to Laverstock, the new cook had started finding ways to annoy her and assert his authority. Finally, she had plucked up the courage to get rid of him. Now, she felt, she was finally the mistress of her own household.

'Bravo, good girl. About time too if you ask me, you can't let people cheat you.'

The two women discussed the war, the food situation, their children born and unborn, their husbands and their servants, until the cheerful figure of Michael de St Aubin approached their table.

He shook their hands formally, sat down carefully, and at first seemed uncertain how to behave with the pair of them, until Kay beckoned him to lean forward, and whispered very loudly, 'So come on, Michael. Tell us about Charlie and Anna. How are they getting on? We want all the gossip. Then we can order lunch.'

Michael leaned back in his chair, beamed broadly and dropped his shoulders. 'I haven't heard any gossip for three years, I was hoping to get it all from you two. Charlie and Anna are like teenagers, very lovey-dovey, as happy as clams.'

'We heard Anna has him round her little finger.' Audrie was relieved that Anna seemed to have settled into married life. 'Gwyneth saw them at Nuwara Eliya and said Anna's transformed him from a crusty old bachelor planter, forty something, into a doting husband, fetching and carrying.'

'Well, yes, I suppose,' Michael grinned. 'They often invite me up, so I see them two or three times a week for dinner. He's still the same with me out on the estate but can't wait to get home and look after her, and around the house he's absolutely charming.'

'Go on, and what about you? Any sign of a girlfriend?'

'I'm fine. Lots of books and magazines to read. But not a chance in hell of meeting anyone.' His shyness disappeared with Audrie's friendly question.

The waiter appeared again and they ordered the special GOH rice and curry lunch. Meat curry, string hoppers, egg rulang, potato and spinach curry, seeni sambal, cabbage and coconut mallung, brinjals and various chutneys, appeared until the table was crowded, as the two waiters made a fuss of serving the various dishes one by one.

'You know what it's like. I may have to resort to the famous Nurses Home Café trick you told me about.' The women both laughed.

'It can't be that bad,' protested Audrie.

'Actually, it's got worse,' Michael confided. 'Charlie used to come down here once a fortnight, often bringing me, usually to pick up cash to pay the estate workers and visit Elephant House to fill the beef box. But now he brings Anna with him, and leaves me up on the estate. They usually stay a couple of nights, play bridge at the Garden Club or Princes. In the daytime, she swims and plays tennis while he's at the Lipton office.'

'Michael,' said Kay, putting down her fork. 'We can soon fix that. Let us know next time you can get down and you can put up with my parents at Justice House. There are often people staying and Mamma often needs extra single men about, to make up the numbers.'

'Stay with you?' Michael seemed taken aback to be considered a suitable guest at Justice House. 'That would be lovely, thank you.' Smiling to himself, he returned to his curry.

'Michael, tell me, what's it like up on the estate?' Audrie asked. 'My Pa was a superintendent near there when I was little, but then he was promoted and we moved to Maskeliya and then down to Colombo. Do you have electric light yet? And is there ever a chance for some fun?'

'No, no electric yet in the bungalow. Still gas lights.' Michael rubbed his chin. 'And shaving in the dark isn't much fun. But I do enjoy the KV Club. I get down there every fortnight or so. It's not bad, there's rugby, tennis, snooker, bridge and of course, a lot of drinking. I'm very careful about that and anyway can't afford it. Our valley gets flooded up to about six feet at least once every year.' He paused to ladle himself another spoonful of the egg rulang. 'In the wet weather, it's just awful; you have to pay particular attention to your feet. Not a very salubrious subject at lunch, but it's very easy to get toe rot or a terrible itch, and we get through tons of talcum powder.'

'It's much the same here,' Kay observed. 'We have to have an electric bar burning in the wardrobes to stop our shoes going green.'

Plates were changed and more dishes arrived. 'I had a green snake in my shower the other day, terrifying,' Michael announced. 'But Charlie keeps an old mamoty there in case, and it came in very useful.'

'Ugh, don't even talk about snakes. I can't stand them,' Audrie shuddered, wrapping her arms round herself.

'We have rat snakes in the roof of the bungalow,' Michael said, ignoring her, so pleased finally to be able to talk to someone different. 'They're giant things, six-foot long, they live under the eaves. Charlie calls them our rat catchers, unpaid. We hear regular slithering noises and squeals as they go to work, but they're harmless to us.'

'Oh, please do stop it,' Audrie urged, staring intently at her plate. 'We used to find them in the bathroom when I was little. Once I was sitting on the loo and there was a snake in the laundry basket next to me. I screamed the house down and one of the servants came and killed it. So do stop. I can't bear even thinking about it.'

'I'm so sorry, Audrie,' Michael apologised, 'I was just rattling on, it's such a delight to see you again, I wasn't thinking.'

'Of course, don't worry.' Audrie picked up her fork to finish her chicken curry.

'You have to watch that waiter,' Kay said later as they paid the bill and strolled back to the reception hall. 'Last week at lunch here with Mamma, we both had the kedgeree and a soda, and it came to one rupee sixty, but he gave us a bill for three twenty. Then, when my mother questioned him, he smiled and said, "But, Lady, I am giving you double portion." Shall we walk?'

As they emerged into the sunlight and the heat of York Street, Kay put up a parasol and they strolled down past Cargill's and across Baillie Street, keeping close to the shop fronts and staying as far as possible in the shade. They paused under a huge tree which spread its vast canopy in the gardens by the clock tower.

'These are wonderful,' said Audrie. 'Have you seen them in the jungle up-country?'

'Not sure,' Michael laughed. 'I'm surrounded by tea all day and I've never been into the jungle proper, just driven through. Just the village near the estate.'

'It's a rain tree.' Audrie recalled playing with Chim in the garden up at Glenugie when they were little. 'There was one on the lawn at home. We used to sit under it in the evenings. At night their leaves fold up into tiny envelopes and the moisture condenses inside.' She reached up and picked a handful of leaves from a low branch. 'Then in the morning when the sun comes up they uncurl again. If you get up really early and stand underneath, you can have a shower.'

They strolled on, past the governor's residence, back towards the port gates. Michael set off towards the Bristol, while Kay and Audrie crossed over towards the GOH. It was now the hottest part of the day, and a water cart drawn by two bullocks trundled past them, while across the street, a sweeper was busy with a long broomstick. In front of the hotel was a solitary rickshaw, parked with its hood up and its shafts down on the ground. Inside, the rickshaw coolie was fast asleep.

Kay nudged Audrie and pointed at the sleeping boy. 'Shall we wake him?'

'Let him sleep. Com's driver is picking me up at the hotel at three. Thank you so much for the lunch. I'll drop you.'

'Darling, that would be lovely. And your news is so wonderful. Before long you'll have to stop walking around in this heat, and put your feet up every afternoon.'

When Audrie wrote to her parents from the Joseph Fraser Nursing Home, proudly announcing the birth of her daughter, Susan, there was no indication of any problems. At first, Susan seemed a normal, healthy child, and Robin, now two and a half, was thrilled with his baby sister.

Colombo, January 1942

Audrie came downstairs carrying Susan on one arm, and a half-drunk cup of tea in her free hand. She turned towards the garden, where Com sat on the back terrace, reading the paper. Outside, the garden boy was pulling out the latest crop of fast-growing weeds, and Robin was playing with a toy elephant, supervised by Nanny as usual.

'Darling,' she announced, 'we're out of Kolynos. Can't say I like the taste, but there's not much else.'

'Hate the stuff. Do please try and find something different this time.'

She went over to her son and stroked his face. 'Hello, darling baby. Good morning, Nanny. Com, we weighed Susan yesterday, and I'm worried she's still not putting on enough weight.'

'What did the doctor say? Is she eating enough?'

'Not worrying, Lady,' the Ayah reassured them as Audrie handed the little girl to her. 'Baby will be fine. I will make sure she has plenty.'

'Listen to this,' Com interjected, 'from last night's *Times*.

Japanese attacks have been repelled in Ipoh and Perak,

and there's an announcement.

In the light of the Japanese attacks in Malaya, the newly appointed Civil Defence Commissioner Mr Goonetilleke has announced plans for an air raid precaution scheme. All doors and windows are to be sealed at night, and all lampshades covered. The police will prosecute anyone showing a light after dark. No evacuation plans are being considered.'

'That's a relief,' Audrie acknowledged. 'But are we really expecting air raids? Good God. Here?' Com folded his paper to the lower part of the page. 'The greatest Danger, it says, with a Capital D, is from Panic, with a capital P.'

'I should think so too.' Audrie poured tea for herself and topped up Com's teacup. 'That was the *On Dit* at the committee last week when we were doing the bandages.' Com turned over the page. A flock of small grey birds which had landed noisily on the terrace, noticed his presence and immediately fluttered off.

He read from the paper. '"*Cargill's is to close at 4 pm in future, as so many of their staff have been called up.*" We may have to think of something like that at Apothecaries. And look here. "*A second contingent of the Ceylon Planters Rifle Corps is to leave for officer training in India, under the command of Neil Garland, son-in-law of the Chief Justice.*"'

'My Lord, when are they off? Did you know they were going? What's Kay going to do?'

'They heard only a few days ago. When we had lunch, Kay said something was up, but she wasn't allowed to tell me what or where, and now there it is in the paper. They're both going.'

'I'm off now. I won't be late. What's happening this evening?'

'We're due at the Moores' for drinks at seven, Jean has some friends from Singapore they're putting up, she wants us all to meet them and help them get settled. I'll call Kay now and see when Neil's actually off; we must say goodbye.'

'I'll tell William to arrange the blackout,' Com reminded her as he prepared to leave. 'There's bound to be a run on curtain material.'

Audrie leaned out of the veranda to check on Robin, and then picked up the paper. Since the news of the Japanese attacks on Hong Kong and Malaya, she had been anxiously following the progress of the new theatre of war, but so far, without thinking if or how it would affect them personally in Ceylon. Although she was worried about the long hours he was working, at least Com had not been called up. Her family in Europe concerned her much more. But now, if the Government thought a blackout was needed here, did that mean they expected bombers over Colombo? Could they be hit by a Blitz like London? Her mother's letters often mentioned bombs falling in Kent and Sussex.

It didn't bear thinking about. She went to her desk to call Kay.

In early January 1942, Com received a brown OHMS envelope containing a chit from a Captain Hopkins, asking him to meet him at room 12 of the Galle Face at eleven o'clock the following morning. 'Don't mention the meeting to anyone,' the note said, 'even to your wife.' There was no explanation. It must be via Jimmy Gardner, Com reasoned, to do with the application to join up, or else a CPRC matter.

Room 12 was on the first floor, at the end of the long corridor, a big corner room with windows onto the sea and the green. Hopkins was rather obtuse at first, asking about Com's work and routine, but he seemed to know a lot about Aberdeen, Com's life in Colombo and also his spare-time hobbies – chess, puzzles and crosswords. Com's name was apparently on a 'technical and scientific register of people whose skills could be useful in specific areas of the war effort'.

Eventually Hopkins came to the point. As Cam had suspected, they had a file on him from his application to the Gordons. They'd lost a man in an important section, he said, who'd gone on leave and failed to return. Would Com help part time in his unit? He'd be a civilian employee, but excused any further training with the CPRC except in emergency. Com swallowed hard. How would he be expected to fit it all in?

'I'd welcome being able to help, do some real war work,' he had finally responded. 'But if you know all this then you'll also know I'm on the reserved list because of the Apothecaries.'

'Of course. How much time do the Apothecaries and Kandy Hotels roles take?' asked Hopkins. Com explained his schedule and asked what the new work involved, but Hopkins wouldn't tell any more about his own job or the identity of his department, until Com had met one or two more people and then if all was well, had agreed to sign the Official Secrets Act.

For Com, already stressed, it would be a serious extra load, but at least it would be real war work at last. He wouldn't be able to explain his whereabouts to any Apothecaries or Kandy Hotels colleagues, and he'd have to work out what to say to Audrie.

Two days later, Com was summoned for a second meeting, this time at the Pembroke College base. On arrival, he was sent from the sentries' gatehouse to an office where he was interviewed again, this time by a plain clothes officer called Yoxall, who gave him some simple substitution puzzles which didn't take long. Behind the main school building there were several long low brick huts, with thatched roofs of palm leaves and whitewashed interiors. Yoxall led him outside, along a concrete path between the huts, to another office where Hopkins and another man, introduced as Hugh Taylor, were waiting. Hopkins was very welcoming, easy-going, but the other man, officious and charmless, just waved a paper at him.

'You will, of course, sign this,' Taylor barked, 'to acknowledge the imperatives of the Official Secrets Act 1920 as amended 1939.' Com signed. 'You can inform your colleagues and your family that you are doing some office work for the war effort. Call it war work. No more than that.'

Finally, Hopkins explained that he was head of the Far East Combined Bureau, and outlined its role in support of Allied code breaking. Colombo was the first line of signal intercept and decoding of the Japanese Navy messages. The local team had first crack at deciphering the most important messages. 'In addition to the wireless operators,' he said, 'there are a few specialists who work on corrupt or broken signals. That's your role. Taylor will brief you, then I'll take you down and introduce you around.' Hopkins nodded to Taylor and left the room.

Taylor spoke for half an hour, in a high-pitched, dry voice which grated, coughing continuously. Com noticed that he had gigantic feet.

The man he was replacing worked under a Norman Scott, Taylor told him. It would be four or five shifts over two or three days a week, a total of fifteen hours. Com was to work alongside several dozen WRENS who'd been specially trained at home and then sent out to Ceylon. They would pay him Rs 300 a month, and an extra petrol allowance, and review in a couple of months.

'In addition to the WRENS, we have some locally hired temporary civilian secretaries, mostly European women,' Taylor added. 'If you should see anyone you know while you're here, you're not to recognise them or speak to them about this work, here or anywhere else.' Com nodded. This must be where Kay's sister Laura is working, he realised, but then started worrying what would happen if he saw her.

Taylor gave him a pass, and a photographer came in to take a picture for his service ID card. Com waited for a while until Hopkins returned and led him out of the hut.

'Come and I'll introduce you to Scott, your section head, and he can give you an idea of what actually happens,' he said, leading Com along a path to yet another long hut, where about twenty service personnel, women and men, all in white uniform, were sitting at desks. They went through to another room.

Norman Scott was fiftyish, small and round with rimless glasses, and almost bald, with a few fluffy hairs on either side of his head. He wore an old beige linen jacket, grey flannel bags, with smartly polished brown brogues. Com thought he looked like Hollywood's version of a professor, the one that's usually the heroine's father.

'I'll give you a full briefing next time, but for now, we'll start you with this,' Scott told him. Hopkins left them together. Com felt distinctly nervous, like a new boy starting school all over again.

Com was in his office at the Apothecaries, telephoning a cargo shipping line agent, to locate a consignment of pharmaceuticals which he'd been promised would be on their next ship from the Cape. Somehow, he doubted it. As he waited, he heard a woman's raised voice in the outer office. Com's senior clerk put his face round the door.

'Mrs Blackwood to see you,' he said.

'What does she want?' Com put down the telephone and swivelled round in his chair. The Blackwoods were a tea-planting family; everybody knew the Blackwoods.

'Com, it's Joyce,' said the voice from outside his door, which was immediately followed by a tall figure in a white suit and hat. Pink in the face, she strode straight up to his desk, stood in front of him and folded her arms.

Com stood up. 'Joyce, how nice to see you. Do please sit…'

'Sorry. Haven't time. It's about the Singapore families.'

Com sat back down. 'What chappies?'

She unfolded her arms, reached into her huge bag and pulled out a clipboard list. 'I don't know if you were in town yesterday? Did you hear about the *Duchess of Bedford*?'

Com leaned back and twiddled his pencil. 'What? Don't say you've invited her to stay?'

'Don't be silly, Com darling. I'm not joking, this is very serious. It's a ship. She arrived in harbour yesterday, escaped from Singapore.' Joyce waited for him to reply but he just nodded as she continued.

'There are about six hundred evacuees, civilian families, some service wives and children, wounded soldiers, all sorts. They seem to have got out just before the city collapsed. It must have been ghastly.' She pulled a green hanky out of her bag and began patting her forehead. 'I was just down at the quay watching them come ashore. There are injured, sick or wounded on stretchers who've gone into hospital or the navy barracks. It's pretty awful. Some are still in shock, but anyway they've nowhere to stay.'

'Can they stay on board while we sort it out?'

'It's being fumigated. Apparently they had a cargo of onions from before the passage, didn't have time to unload, and it went foul.

Anyway she, the ship, has to go on to the Cape. We, I mean, I'm on the committee; we're trying to house some of them here, either for the duration or until they can get home.' She exhaled, flourishing her handkerchief, apparently having finished what she'd come to say.

'Yes, Joyce, sit down, you'll explode. What can I do?'

Joyce lowered herself into the chair opposite Com, and paused for a moment. She leaned forwards and helped herself to a glass from the bottle of water on his desk.

'Can you and Audrie take some, say a couple? At Laverstock?'

Com hesitated for a few seconds, not sure if his new war work would allow him to spend so much time with others, without their discovering what he was doing.

'Yes, of course, if we move everything out of my dressing room, we'd have an extra room, we could do a couple.'

'You are a saint.' Joyce wrote in her notebook, carefully put away the pencil and her green hanky in her vast bag, turned and left his office in pursuit of her next victim.

Nervously, Com telephoned Audrie, to tell her the news. 'Of course we must,' she said. Two days later, Olive and Gerald Rayner, who had lost almost everything in Singapore – their clothes, most of their money, and as soon became clear, their good manners – became their guests.

Coming from Singapore, the Rayners were obviously accustomed to expatriate life, but not, it seemed, to Ceylon ways. When Com brought them to the house, and William stepped out to lift one of the Rayners' battered suitcases from the car boot, the refugee almost screamed at him. 'Leave that case alone, you bloody idiot, never touch my things!' By the end of their first day at Laverstock, they'd already upset two more of the servants, which didn't endear them to Audrie either.

The houseboy complained to William that when he offered to help unpack, Mrs Rayner had yelled at him so much that he'd thought she was going to hit him. Perhaps, Audrie wondered, they were accustomed to treating their Chinese staff like slaves. She spoke to William later.

'Our new guests have been through a very stressful time,' she reminded the Appu. 'Please make sure the staff know that they should not worry if Mr and Mrs Rayner seem a little difficult. And let me know if anything unusual happens.'

'Yes, Lady,' replied William. 'Very difficult. I will keep you informed.'

But both Lady and Appu could see it wouldn't be plain sailing.

***

When Com returned to the briefing room at HMS *Pembroke*, Norman Scott was easy-going, a complete contrast to the officious Taylor. He asked Com to sit, but didn't do so himself, constantly pacing up and down.

'This is where the real decoding work is done,' Scott declared. 'The rest of them are really just admin and support.' Com opened his green notebook.

'With a little help from the US Navy,' Scott revealed, 'we're reading the main Japanese fleet code.' Com's pen dashed across the page as he tried to keep up.

Many messages used military and official titles, Scott explained. 'Combined with the fact that the Japanese only make changes to the code every three to six months, this gives us a toehold.'

Com scribbled notes as fast as he could, wishing he'd studied shorthand. Scott lit cigarette after cigarette and the air in the small room was soon blue.

Messages always came in groups of five letters, Com understood, but decodes were often corrupted en route, with several letters missing and very rarely a complete group. He watched as Scott pointed to a series of examples on the wall.

'Skeletons of phrases appear,' he explained, 'and need to be completed. We need you to reconnect them.'

He grinned at Com over his glasses. 'All that time wasted on the *Times* crossword will finally be of some use.' Com smiled back but it was unnerving that these people knew all about him.

One of the easiest ways into a code, Scott went on, was finding repeated sequences. Most Jap service radio operators insisted on sending routine messages at precisely the same time every day. Once the format of these messages had been recovered, or guessed at, they could very often be predicted. A message sent at 0900 hours every morning by a Jap operator nearly always said he had nothing to report. Working backwards, that would help give the cipher. 'Given practice,' Scott insisted, 'you'll be able to read messages quickly.'

'They use formal phrases,' he continued, 'such as "I have the honour to inform your Excellency" – names of ships, locations, commanders, time and date, and similar repeated information that we can easily verify. That's what you'll be looking out for.' Com nodded weakly, thinking he'd write it all down as soon as he could, and wondering where this would lead and if he had a snowflake's chance in hell of ever understanding it all. Or any of it. Scott came and stood over him, pointing down at his notebook. 'The notebook is acceptable. But I'd be grateful if you could remember all this, and not repeat it. Ever. We cannot allow your work notes or official materials to leave the building.'

'Of course,' Com told him. But he knew he'd have to write it down or forget. 'I'll leave it in my locker,' he reassured Scott.

'And just in case nobody's explained,' Scott continued, 'this place is absolutely secure, so we don't allow any cleaners in here and you'll have to clean up after yourself. We all do.'

'Come down to have a look and meet the WIOs,' Scott concluded. 'It'll help you understand your job if you see them at work.'

He led the way out of the office and along a concrete path to a green door with a mosquito gate across it. They stepped into a room with a desk in the centre and along the wall, several men in blue RAF shirts or white RN uniform, sets of headphones over their heads, and pencils moving quickly across the pads in front of them. Several large fans overhead maintained a breeze which shuffled the piles of papers on the desks and tables around the room.

Scott gestured to Com to sit down next to one of them, who raised his head, nodded, and put out his hand to shake.

'Armour, Eric Armour, from Selby, WIO.' Com saw a shiny, pointed nose, and pinched, probably underfed features, but a welcoming smile. 'You new?'

'Sutherland, Robert, from Aberdeen. In Ceylon, no, but here, yes. How d'ye do?'

The Wireless Intercept Officer, or YO as he would now learn to call them, touched his finger to his lips and sat back again with his arms folded across his chest, watching the second hand on the wall clock creep towards the hour. 'They're always on time,' he murmured. 'I'm waiting for Itchy. Watch and listen carefully. Don't say a word.'

'Itchy?'

'Wait and see. He's always on time. Now shh.'

In front of him on the desk, a DST 100 receiver, similar to the ones Com had trained on in Calcutta, hummed and waited patiently. Putting his headphones on, Armour reached forward and turned up the volume dial. He cranked the frequency wheel very slowly, until 3845 kilocycles appeared in the tiny window. Com leaned forward to watch.

As the second hand hit the 12 mark, Armour nodded to Com as he heard the far-away fist tap out the first digit of the day, announcing to the world that this particular Japanese naval radio operator was up and transmitting.

'Right on time,' Armour murmured. His pencil shot across the page as he began writing down the five digit groups that came steadily through his headphones. It was fascinating. Three minutes later the Jap signed off with QSL, which Com knew was the international code for 'acknowledge'. Learning Morse fifteen years ago on a Calcutta Battalion course was going to be of some use after all.

The YO quickly retuned the frequency to 3975 and listened as the other Japanese operator acknowledged Itchy's transmission by repeating the first ten groups of the message and then went silent.

'Thanks, laddies,' Armour said out loud. He tore off the top sheet of the intercept pad, and waved it over his head, calling 'Mouse.' A clerk hurried forward, took the paper from his hand, and pushed through a door to the next room. Armour moved the frequency handle on the DST 100 to 3655, sat back watching the clock and waited for his next target to emerge from the high frequency ether.

'This next one we call Nicky,' Armour said. 'That's the second best characteristic of the Japanese naval radio operators – always on a set schedule and bang on frequency.'

'And the first?'

'The first is the unique way any operator taps out the dots and dashes for any of the letters and groups. It's the same for all of us.' Every operator had a distinctive 'fist' and the YO had nicknamed each of the dozen or so he listened to every day.

'How on earth,' Com asked, 'd'you learn to hear and get it all down so fast?'

'Practice, laddie. Practice.' Com must have been at least ten years older than Armour, but he let the YO go on. 'You start out sitting next to an expert and both copying down what you hear, then you compare notes, and pretty soon you can catch almost everything. But when we can't get it, that's when people like you come in.'

Com told him he couldn't wait. 'Where do the signals came from?'

'All over,' he said. 'We're listening to ships and shore stations all over – the South China Sea, the Malacca Straits, and the Indian Ocean. There's even a signal we think may be coming from here.'

'Here? Colombo?'

'Or nearby. We had a report,' Armour confided, 'from a YO who monitored a strong signal with a fist he'd never heard before. Not the usual frequency. Didn't get the message down. We had it checked. They're using RDF to find where it could be from. We're instructed to keep a watch out. See you next time.'

Audrie was already in bed when he got home well after eleven. Suddenly, Com was involved in the world of espionage, and it was not easy to behave as if nothing had changed. 'War work,' he said, hoping she understood. 'Not allowed to talk about it.'

'As long as it's not another woman,' Audrie sighed. 'Now, my darling hard-working husband, come to bed.'

As the news from Singapore worsened, the order came that all members of the CPRC were to be embodied full time. There were to be no more volunteers. That weekend was his last parade, but he couldn't explain to Audrie what was going on. Or to anyone.

As he drove home on the day that the Japanese invaded Burma, Com saw anti-aircraft guns being installed along Galle Face Green. Food restrictions had been introduced, even in private, he noted that day, although how they'd be enforced, nobody could guess. One main dish and one side dish were allowed, or two side dishes and one rice dish. How did they think people would manage? No food ships had got through for more than a week.

The Times of Ceylon, 1942

DEPARTMENT OF CIVIL DEFENCE

Colombo Air Raid
Precautions Scheme
Casualty Service

Help is required from ladies to make First Aid
dressings for the ARP casualty service.
Would those who are willing to help be so kind
as to call at the Girl Guides headquarters,
Edinburgh Crescent, Colombo, any time between
9am and 12pm and 2pm and 4pm on week days,
when Mrs P.J.Chissell or Mrs R.W.Sutherland
would show them the type of dressings which
we require and how to make them.

C. Gunasekera
Chief Medical Officer of Health

When the Colombo paper told of the final fall and surrender of Singapore, every expatriate in Ceylon was horrified to learn that the Japanese had taken more than eighty thousand European prisoners.

'Darling, listen. *The Gordon Highlanders were among the newly arrived forces sent to help relieve the defenders of the city,*' he read out. He quickly decided not to tell Audrie that Jimmy Gardner had probably been among the casualties.

From the papers, and gossip at the clubs and his office, Com knew that the war was coming closer. Refugees were arriving almost daily from Singapore, on ships which had been bombed as they escaped the carnage. Many of the bigger hotels, the Galle Face included, had turned large public rooms into temporary dormitories to provide accommodation for these refugees, and Com had been astonished to see that along the harbour area, where the Japanese might be expected to attack, many locals had hung Japanese flags out of windows in anticipation of their arrival. Thousands of British and Indian servicemen were arriving on troopships to reinforce the local native and expatriate forces, and he had already heard talk of evacuating European families.

An official Government letter confirmed that as head of the Apothecaries, with its role to supply essential medical and pharmaceutical supplies, he was reserved and must stay in post. Probably Hopkins' doing, he noted. God knows what he could do about Audrie and the children.

On 3 March, at FECB, a decoded message suggested that five large Japanese submarines from Penang were operating across the Indian Ocean. FECB's YOs were reading much useful radio traffic, some even in plain language, and clearly, something big was in the air. Hopkins hadn't been seen for several days.

'Let's hope there's no repeat of the Singapore debacle,' Com confided to his notebook. 'I don't think we have more than five defence guns and certainly only a few planes. Saw a flight of Hurricanes come in to Ratnapura yesterday. But we rely on the Navy as usual.'

Within weeks of their arrival, the Rayners were treating Laverstock as their own. Gerald would shut himself in his room for hours, and Com at first put his erratic behaviour down to the horror of the war in Singapore. The Rayners constantly asked to borrow the car, and clearly didn't understand or chose to ignore, the concept of petrol rationing. One day, Com even saw Rayner coming out of the GOH, and get into Com's car, but when he asked about it later at home, Rayner just said he'd been for a walk around Fort.

Early in March, Com was alone at the breakfast table, on the back veranda, squeezing a lime onto his slices of papaya. The kitchen door opened silently. William brought *The Times of Ceylon* and handed it to him, pointing at a boxed headline on the front page. Com stared at it, folded the paper to a quarter and propped it against the fruit bowl in the centre of the breakfast table.

'Darling? Audrie? Are you there?' he called to the open door.

'Lady coming,' said William, and vanished through to the kitchen. A minute later, Audrie, in a pink silk dressing gown and with a towel round her head, came downstairs and sat opposite him.

'I'm concerned about the little one.' Audrie sat down with her hands in her lap and looked straight at her husband. Susan was now eight months old. 'Surely she should be putting on more weight?'

'What did the doc say yesterday?'

'"Just to be patient, she's coming along," he said, "perfectly all right, just a matter of time."'

'Let's hope it's not anything serious.'

'I'll take her back to the clinic in a week.'

'I'll come with you. But look at this.'

'What is it? More bandages?'

'There's a big announcement about the defence of the island.' He took another sip of tea and began to read.

In defence of Lanka. If an enemy force landed anywhere near my home what should I do?

'Shoot them?'

'Of course. But that's not what this says.' He folded the paper. Audrie picked at the grapes in the fruit bowl and instantly thought of her mother.

I should remember that my countrymen in the Ceylon Defence Force have been reinforced by many soldiers, sailors and airmen from Britain and India and that they are working together to defend my homeland. It is up to me therefore to play my part, and this is how I can do it.

Audrie started to giggle, and Com frowned at her.

One: I will keep the roads absolutely clear... We can't use the car … absolutely clear for the troops by staying in my house or garden and so enable them to move quickly. This will also save me from the dangers of air attack, or being run over by lorries, or of being shot in mistake for the enemy.

'What on earth? How could they mistake me for the enemy?'

'And we'll have to let go the bullock.'

'Bullock? Are you pulling my leg?' Audrie's mouth dropped open.

'It's serious,' Com laughed.

Two: If I happen to be driving a Bullock cart I will drive it off the road into the lane or a plantation, let loose the bullock and make him fast to a tree or a post.

Three: If I happen to be driving a motor vehicle, I will drive it off the road, into a lane or plantation, and then take the rotor out of the distributor. I will take the rotor away and make for my home or some neighbouring house and I will stay there quietly.

'Oh, and the bike. Darling, I'll have to let the air out of the bicycle tyres.'

'Bicycle?' He read on…

If I possess a bicycle I will deflate both tyres and then hide the cycle in one place and the pump in another.

'But this isn't compulsory, is it? Only if there's an invasion. Why do they think there's going to be an invasion?' Audrie held her teacup in both hands and stared at him over the top.

'It's because of what happened at Singapore. They think the Japs will try and take Ceylon. I'd like to see them try. I'd better get on to office before they stop us using the car.'

Com hurriedly finished his tea and set off upstairs to find his jacket, while Audrie picked up the paper and read the announcement for herself.

Four days later, the news Com had been dreading was staring at him from the front page of the paper.

'Darling, listen, I was expecting this. I didn't mention it because I'd hoped it would never happen. But they've decided, they're going to evacuate all non-essential European families.'

He folded the paper and read: 'Evacuation Advice from Commander-in-Chief.

Admiral Sir Geoffrey Layton, Commander-in-Chief, has issued the following statement.

In view of the unsettled state now existing and the problems relating to food supply etc., the following instructions regarding evacuation are issued for the guidance of all concerned:

All persons not normally resident in Ceylon and who are not employed in essential war work must arrange to leave as soon as passages are available for them. This includes the wives and children of Naval, Military and Air Force personnel.

With regard to residents of Ceylon, non-Ceylonese women with young children who are not employed on war work are advised to leave as soon as they can conveniently do so.'

'Darling, I'm sorry. So very sorry. But this means us.'

Audrie paled. 'What do we do? Go home? Can't you come? Why must you stay?'

'You know. The Apothecaries. I'm reserved. And this new war work. But no, not worth going home. It won't be more than a few weeks or months. Just until the invasion scare is over. They recommend South Africa, so you can get back here quickly when it's over. But you can go all the way home if you'd rather. It won't be nearly so risky as last time.'

His stomach churned as he lied to his wife. FECB were monitoring signals from at least four Japanese submarines in the Indian Ocean. She couldn't stay, of course not, what with the terrible stories they had heard about Japanese cruelty to the Chinese and European inhabitants of Singapore. And everybody suspected that Colombo and Trinco with their deep-water harbours would be their next targets. But if she went, then a passage nearly five thousand miles across the ocean to the Cape could be even more dangerous.

Audrie was silent. She refused to allow herself to cry, but tears soon started and she wiped them away with the back of her hand. Com looked steadily at her, trying to keep himself from showing his agony while his insides felt as though they were being screwed into tiny balls of wire.

'Chin up. I'll drop in at the terminal and make you a reservation, it can't be for long. It's for the best. Better to be safe. I promise you'll be all right, Mrs Sutherland.'

––––––––––––

The guard at the dock gate stepped forward from his sentry box. Com rolled down the window. Audrie sat in the back with Susan in her arms and Robin on the seat beside her.

'Are you taking passage, sir?' He bent down to look inside the car. 'Tickets?'

'Sad to say, we are.' Com's smile was grim as he held out the document.

'Please, going right ahead.' The guard gave a rather un-military salute.

Com let out the clutch and the Austin crawled through the dock entrance. Once through, they emerged into a different world, among a sea of humanity which resembled a disorganised anthill, until a pattern became visible.

Dozens of European families were milling about by the entrance to the passenger terminal building, as more and more were dropped off and began the process of registration for the passage. Around them, piles of baggage lay beside each group, servants unloaded suitcases and boxes from car boots and roofs, children ran around and in between the legs of their parents.

White-uniformed shipping line staff hurried between the small groups, checking names, while loading supervisors shouted orders at the porters staggering to and fro under the weight of sea trunks and boxes. The general hubbub of the crowd was amplified by the occasional hoots of ships, the regular three blasts of the passenger tenders reversing out of the terminal to bustle across to the great liner in the harbour, and the warning whistles of cranes loading.

They parked near the corner of the white arrivals building. 'There she is.'

'That's not *Orontes!*' Gleaming black and white and with smoke rising from her twin funnels, a sleek liner, twice the size of *Orontes*, lay at anchor, just at the edge of the long breakwater, her nose pointing north out to sea, as though impatient to get under way.

'It's *Eindhoven*,' Com said, shading his eyes from the sun. 'Dutch. I've read about her. Brand new just before the war, on the America run. Converted to a troopship now. More than twenty-five knots. The bloody Japs won't catch you in her.' Audrie said nothing.

Robin, now three, was pulling on the blue leather harness which held him from running away in the melee. Com lifted his son up on his shoulder to get a better view. 'Look at the big ship. It'll be your home for the next few weeks.'

'Ship,' came the response.

'Darling,' he turned to his wife, who was struggling with the baby and her hand luggage. 'I'll take him and park the car, and catch you up in the queue.'

She found the queue, and gradually shuffled forward towards the reception hut beside the dock buildings. Finally, a large family group moved away from the window, and Audrie reached the front. A harassed-looking Orient Line clerk, all in white, looked up from the booking sheet.

'Mrs Sutherland and family, three of us, double cabin, C Deck,' she said, handing over the tickets.

The young clerk pulled a white cloth from his shorts pocket and wiped his forehead. Audrie hitched the baby up on her hip.

'I'm so sorry, madam, but the cabin you've booked is no longer available,' he said, looking flustered. 'We've had to re-arrange everything. It's not an Orient Line ship, it's Dutch. One class only. She was converted to a troopship. You'll be sharing a cabin on D Deck, with another lady and her little boy. We have an extra seven hundred Netherlands service personnel on board and the Line has been instructed to re-arrange all the accommodation.' He looked very relieved to have finished the explanation.

'I'm sorry, but that's ridiculous. My husband booked us into a first class cabin. I can't be asked to share when I've got two babies.'

'I'm sorry, madam. Since Singapore there's no space anywhere.' He took a deep breath. 'We're doing the best we can, but all the B & C Deck cabins have been allocated to the Dutch officers. And they are sharing too. Here are your cabin details, D42. You'll be on the third launch out; they start loading passengers in twenty minutes.'

Audrie stared blankly at him. 'But what about my children?'

'Here we are, darling.' Com appeared. 'What's up?'

Audrie repeated the purser's story. Other women and families, behind Audrie in the line, crowded round them to catch the news.

'What on earth does this mean?' Audrie was now starting to panic. 'How can I look after these two with other people in the way? How could they throw out bona fide passengers with bookings?'

Com's face darkened. 'I'll speak to Angus McLaren. Even with military on board, surely the Line can't be forced to treat its civilian passengers this way?'

'I'm so sorry, sir, the instructions come from Mr McLaren himself; the Line has orders from the top, the C-in-C, Ceylon. And because it's not our ship, everything is out of our control.'

'Nothing you can do?' Com felt cold and hot at the same time. Suddenly, instead of his dry impersonal FECB office at Pembroke, the war was coming to his family, his private life. And it was his wife, not him, who must suffer. And poor darling, she'd already been torpedoed once.

'I'm so sorry, sir, again. It's the war. Since Singapore we've been all over the place. But it's a very big ship, sir, fast, with many modern facilities and trained crew. I'm sure Madam will be comfortable.'

Com turned to his wife. It was bad enough for Audrie, to be setting out on a five-thousand-mile passage, in wartime, travelling alone with children again, after what happened to *Orama*. But now she wouldn't even have privacy.

'Darling, it's no good, I'm so, so sorry.'

'It's not your fault…'

'But I wanted… after the last time, I so much wanted you to be safe and comfortable with these two.'

Audrie had been terrified at the idea of being on her own with the two babies, twenty-four hours a day. Since Robin and then Susan had been born, Nanny had always been nearby. Why couldn't her own mother be there to help? Shut up, she told herself, you're twenty-six. You're English. Grow up. Cope with it.

'Yes, I know.' She grimaced and pushed her hair back with the back of her hand. 'I'm sure I'll be fine.'

'Will you be all right? I mean really all right?' He knew there was absolutely nothing he could do to help, except pray.

'Of course. darling sad husband.' She kissed him. 'Don't fuss. I'm sure they'll do their best. A few days, a week or so, and it will be over.'

'Here we are, madam. D42, D Deck, the tender number is eight. *Bon voyage.*' Audrie gave the purser her old-fashioned look.

'*Bon voyage?* I should say so.' She took the tickets, picked up her handbag, hitched Susan up on her hip, and set off towards the landing stage, Com following with Robin and the cabin bags.

Half an hour later, after farewells and tears and kisses and hugs between all four of them, Audrie stepped into the launch alongside thirty other weary European women, settled the two children, and turned to wave to her husband as they motored out to the waiting ship. Back on the quayside, Com suddenly looked very lonely.

On board, as Audrie climbed up from the water-level access deck to her cabin, with Susan in her arms and a steward carrying Robin, they were met at the top by a Dutch stewardess, who stretched out to take the baby. To Audrie, she looked like an angel, clean, wholesome, capable, in a dark blue uniform and a starched white apron; she wanted nothing more than to hug and kiss her. Finally, they arrived at cabin D42 and Audrie, exhausted, slumped onto the bunk, settled her children and waited to meet her cabin companion.

The Colombo Harbour Master noted in his log that at zero fifteen hours, on 19 March 1942, the converted Dutch liner *Eindhoven*, 36,287 tons, departed for Durban, South Africa, carrying 770 Netherlands military and naval personnel and 600 European passengers.

Laverstock, Melbourne Avenue, Bambalapitya, 19th March 1942

Yesterday was surely the blackest day in our lives. I watched the ship going over the horizon and it looked such a hell of a big target, I thought of last time and was quite sick. To have to leave you to it when you were already completely tired out was just the most awful thing that's ever happened.

People keep saying that it's never so bad as you think, that once the ship gets going and things get straightened out it won't be so bad, but that is no consolation to me at all. It seems that all the bad luck we have falls on you only darling, and there is nothing I can do about it, but please God you will be all right sweetheart and manage to stick it out.

Once you've got to Durban and then on to the Cape we can start trying to be cheerful.

Queen's Hotel, Kandy, 23rd March 1942

I do hope that as soon as you get to Cape Town and settle in, you call in a specialist. The Manns were on the boat before you and will now be there. It might even be a good idea to put Susan in a nursing home for a week or two for observation and a scientific diet. It would serve the double purpose of giving you a rest and making absolutely certain about her.

I'll send you all the money I can each month, whatever I have left, as it will be safe in Africa in any case and you can build up a spot of capital in case of emergency. You can let me know from time to time how the balance stands but I expect you'll find Africa pretty expensive living.

I don't think it will be very long before we have you back again.

Laverstock, 30th March 1942

I'm hoping that by the time you get this you have put the dreadful voyage behind you and are looking forward to a pleasant one back. I expect young Robin is already talking with the Zulu accent.

It was the Rayners' wedding anniversary and they celebrated by taking me to a Chinese restaurant where we had to eat a lot of indigestible and unpronounceable food. He was an electrical engineer and they lived in Japan during the early 30s before they moved to Singapore. I thank God you are all safe and I send all my love.

When I brought all the photocopied pages home from the museum, it became clear that Com had never told Audrie about his war work. Censorship prevented him and other Colombo husbands from sharing news with family in South Africa. Instead, Com had used his notebook to record events in the city. And at the end of March, the war finally arrived over Ceylon.

20th March 1942 *Word went round the WIOs that a spy is at work in Colombo. Somewhere in town they've identified signals from a concealed transmitter. Wherever he's sending from, his message 'I have the honour to inform your Excellency of Royal Navy and commercial shipping movements in Colombo…' was got down and easy to break. The direction finders have only a few minutes to fix his whereabouts, so it can't take long.*

22nd March 1942 *In Kandy. Should have stayed in Colombo. Just as I was leaving yesterday we received an order that the Norris Road bookshop was commandeered for an ARP post, and we had to be out within 48 hours.*

23rd March 1942 *The newest JN-25 adaptation has been broken. We're reading useful stuff every day. Jap naval forces are entering the Indian Ocean. Armour told me they'd intercepted a message about* a carrier force in the area of 'D', and an air raid on 'DG' planned for early April. But no solid idea yet where D could mean. Could be Madras or Calcutta or us.

Gussie Richards threw a party at the Galle Face last night, all Singapore people except me. Those Singapore people can drink – five finger whiskies every time. They are also the most frightful defeatists and some of them ought to be locked up, especially the women. Richard Quibell was 'bomb shocked' and when he got to Java he had lost his memory.

25th March 1942 Couldn't believe it, Orontes came into Colombo harbour today. She is a troopship now, and part of a convoy carrying personnel & equipment. She was still recognisable in spite of being repainted in camouflage colours. We weren't told where she'd come from or where she's sailing next. She's half the size of Eindhoven. But it was comforting to see her and remember our Home Leave.

28th March 1942 The 'DG' target is Colombo. One Jap talking to another in plain view, KO RON BO. Navy going full tilt, everyone rushing about. If they are going to attack, it won't be long now. So relieved Audrie got away. All full time staff leave cancelled. Ammunition is being distributed to all CPRC. I have to come to Pembroke in uniform from now on.

4th April 1942 Saturday afternoon: on duty last night. A Jap fleet is heading for Ceylon, spotted by one of the RAF. Dropped in to the Garden Club on the way home. The word is out but we can't talk about the news.

5th April 1942 Easter Sunday evening. Filled up the tank with full ration. Staying with the Prestons for Saturday near Mt Lavinia. They're leaving in a few days for Durban. At dinner Angela insisted we all come with her to the early Easter service. She said we should all pray to God that the Japanese would be stopped. So we all humoured her and set off.

During the service, everyone went quiet as we could hear the sound of a flight of planes and then bombs. I hurried out of the church, hoping another Singapore disaster couldn't have developed overnight. I drove straight to the top of the beach, scanned the whole bay and then out to sea, there wasn't a single craft or ship to be seen. I hurried back to

HMS Pembroke. As I came up Galle Road past the house, there were Jap aircraft over the hotel ahead of me, coming from the sea, and with no apparent opposition. They were so low that I could see the crew in the cockpits. They flew towards the RAF base at Ratmalan, inland. There was smoke rising up ahead over the city.

It really did seem that the battle had started. The sharp crack of the guns along the Green was continuous. Perhaps a separate flight was attacking ships in the harbour. Thank God Audrie and the babies got away. Suddenly as I rattled past the GFH, a 'plane crashed down in the garden behind, and a few seconds later another into the sea along the Green. I could see a stream of Ceylonese getting out of town as fast as their carts or legs could carry them.

At HMS Pembroke everyone on duty was issued with a rifle and ammo, even the civilians. But by the time we were all ready the raid was over and most of the noise had stopped. The air raid sirens wailed the 'all clear' and then all seemed very quiet. I went home and changed into my CPRC uniform.

Later in the afternoon, Nelly and I came across a Jap aircraft that had come down. It was completely burnt out, but still intact, with the bodies of the two men inside.

Monday 6th April 1942 *The Colombo Times says that the RAF lost 35 aircraft, and the Japanese 25. But probably the true result has been concealed for fear of causing panic. But there has been panic, probably because of the gossip from these refugees about what the Japs did in Singapore, bombing civilians. Thousands of staff and workers have fled inland leaving the harbour and shops empty.*

Thursday 9th April 1942 *Another alarm this morning. A spot of gunfire and the drone of planes etc. But as far as I know no bombs dropped. I think the RAF boys were ready for them again but we'll probably get more news later.*

It turns out there was a raid on Trinco harbour, the carrier Hermes and three others were sunk. These were the men we saw at the United Services club last week. I got fed up with the shelter and went out to have a look see but there wasn't any excitement except a few of our own planes buzzing around.

Sunday 12th April 1942 *HMS Dorsetshire and HMS Cornwall have both been sunk by Jap bombers. Hundreds more of the boys who were here two weeks ago have been killed.*

Monday 13th April *1942 Business is in a pretty awful state. I hear only 150 of Walker's 3500 workers turned up on Monday after the first air raid. Only 14 of our 400 furniture workmen turned up yesterday. The rest are still hiding up-country. All the shops are closed and the staff haven't been able to get their midday meal. I've started a canteen on the premises for the time being. Yesterday I did a spot of manual labour at the docks. All the ship's company of the navy ships in harbour or nearby are helping Ceylon volunteers unload at the docks. All the labourers and dock workers have run away into the jungle, so we were a couple of hundred, all European men looking very odd in our vests and shorts, puffing away on the ropes and cranes to help unload the ships so they could get away before the Japs return.*

I worked steadily for four solid hours until I went back on duty to Pembroke. Heaven knows when the other chaps got finished because the barges were only half unloaded by then. Now I've done my ankle in. Most of the navy code breaker people have been moved, not told where to. There are only two left, so now it's just us and the civilian wireless operators left here. Hopkins has vanished as well, haven't seen him about for more than four days.

Laverstock, Melbourne Avenue. 8th April 1942
My darling, back in Colombo I achieved my ambition last night by whacking the chess champion Richardson. I feel if only I'd studied half as hard at university as I do at chess I'd have been a professor or something by now.

I continue to be a spot irritated, to say the least, with these two guests in the bungalow. They should have been evacuated to the Antarctic, not here. Rayner is constantly avoiding me, and always on edge and irritated. He goes into the bedroom and locks the door at all hours. Mrs Rayner bosses the Appu and behaves as if she owned the Ruddy place. And a spot too possessive. She came in with me yesterday morning to do some shopping, finished at 11.30 and if you please took the car back to the bungalow without even saying please – these little things get my goat. I'll make an effort one of these days and get them out.

Thursday, 16th April 1942
Darling, I'm laid up with this blasted sprained ankle. The bone was bruised and it always takes time to heal properly. I expect to be here a few days more before I can move it sufficiently to get to office. Meanwhile I'm lying in a long chair beside the telephone and trying to conduct the Apothecaries from here. It's rather sickening, this enforced idleness, as there is such an awful lot to do. All the chaps in Fort, old and young, go straight to the jetties after work and put in a couple of hours' manual labour. Damn good exercise, and very essential. It's not much fun sitting here with my leg up.

On board *Eindhoven*, Audrie felt physically and emotionally exhausted. The stress of the last week, packing and preparing for the passage, had left her no time to think. Lying awake in her cabin, she wasn't so much worried for the ship, but for Com and the possibility that the Japanese might attack Ceylon. Now, with the help she was given by the nurses, she could start to recover her strength. After a day or two, she was surprised at how calm she felt inside. Having been through storms and submarine attacks, she began to believe she could cope with anything the world could throw at her.

Audrie and Com had expected *Eindhoven* to sail directly to Cape Town. But just one day out to sea, an announcement confirmed that they would be disembarked at Durban instead. It would mean reducing their passage by a thousand miles, at least three days fewer to spend in the risky areas where Japanese submarines were known to be patrolling.

But I'm supposed to be in Cape Town, she wondered. How would she get there? It was no use fretting. Something would happen.

After eight days at sea, *Eindhoven* poured its cargo of humanity onto the quaysides of Durban. Once ashore with the children, the reality of her situation looked impossible. She still had no idea where to stay, how to get to Cape Town, what was wrong with Susan, or how to find out. She started to feel panicky. But once through the ocean terminal, she and the other evacuees were greeted by a committee of Durban ladies, who, like their Colombo counterparts, were busy with arrangements for the evacuees to stay while they found their feet. After queuing for an hour, trying to keep the children quiet, Audrie was handed a room allocation at the Royal Hotel.

'Very near,' the woman said kindly, 'opposite City Hall, just five minutes in a cab. One of the porters will help you with your bags.'

Once installed, Audrie put the children straight to bed and slept herself, although the room seemed to rock as though she were still on board ship. The next morning, she was ready to face her situation. So far, so good, but they were still fifteen hundred miles from Cape Town. She needed to get there soon, to find somewhere to live, and visit the bank where Com had sent funds for her. All his letters would be delivered there. But there was nobody at her side to help, she was on her own now. She'd have to cope.

The Royal Hotel's kindly receptionists promised to see if they could help. A few hours later, as Audrie sat with Susan and Robin in the lobby, a woman in uniform approached with a solution. The Orange Express was offering special terms for evacuees on their weekly service from Durban to the Cape, arriving two nights and three days later. Leaving the children with a hotel nursery nurse, Audrie walked to the station and booked a sleeping compartment, to share with another woman and her child.

Once the journey started, Audrie felt relieved that she was finally making progress. Waiting around was always more exhausting than actually doing something. On the train, her new companion, another Ceylon evacuee, was pleasant and helpful, but Audrie felt a little embarrassed that her small boy behaved much better than Robin on the long journey. Two days in a compartment with the three children was an exhausting test of patience for both mothers, but as Audrie wrote, they were able to help each other and take it in turns to walk the corridor and visit the washrooms with the children.

Arriving at Cape Town, Audrie took a taxi out of town to Princes, a comfortable hotel in the suburb of Newlands, where the staff at the Royal had arranged a room. Princes was a large, gothic Victorian relic, obviously built by a speculator who'd imagined in the 1900s that travel and tourism to Cape Town and the surrounding areas would expand exponentially. In red brick and with gabled roofs, it resembled a smaller and less important St Pancras, and was in need of exterior paint and interior updating. As they arrived, the front looked ominous and uninspiring, but there were extensive gardens at the rear, with a small pool and space for children to play. The reception staff were delightful, and clearly Audrie and the children would be a welcome change from their usual clientele of business travellers.

After seeing several rooms, she chose a large one on the second floor, well-furnished with two beds, and a cot was quickly supplied for Susan. There was a small balcony, unfortunately not child-proof, but where she could sit out and see Table Mountain. Downstairs, there were two usually empty public rooms where she and other mothers could take their children to play during the daytime.

At Barclays in Cape Town, a welcome airmail was waiting from Com, which explained the mess at the Colombo Dockside.

> *Angus was not to blame, darling. He had been given the whole ship and his promises about travelling in comfort were quite genuine. It was the navy who stepped in at the last moment and commandeered 2/3 of the ship. I can imagine your feelings, landing on a strange continent all alone. I've been sitting worrying and wondering how you got the kids and the luggage off the ship, how you managed to pack, how you found accommodation and how you managed to leave the kids and find the bank.*

Back at Princes later, reading the letter again, Audrie began to feel proud of herself. Com was right, as usual, she had felt very wobbly arriving alone in a strange country. But so much had happened already, she was managing, and she could give herself a pat on the back. She had now been away from Com for two weeks, and life in Melbourne Avenue seemed eons away. But the longer she'd been on her own, the more she felt she could cope with whatever happened next. Once she'd settled at the hotel, Susan's development would be her priority.

One morning at the Princes, Audrie was circulating the breakfast room buffet, selecting cereal and fruit for herself and Robin, and waiting for a milk drink to be prepared for Susan. At their table, her son was discussing something important with his bear, while the baby gurgled quietly in her carrycot.

'What's Putupap? It looks a lot like porridge,' said a voice at her side. An obviously English woman was smiling at her, while curiously stirring a bowl on the buffet.

'It is, nearly, but made of maize,' Audrie laughed. 'I asked the same question last week.' It was a relief to find someone in a similar situation. 'How did you finish up here?'

'We were chucked out of Cairo,' the newcomer explained as they returned to their adjoining tables. 'Rommel got a bit too close for comfort.' With the Germans advancing towards Egypt, she said, the British authorities in Cairo had taken a similar decision to those in Colombo – expatriate civilian wives and families must leave. As a result, Joan Whiteshield and her two children had found their way to the Cape and the same hotel.

The two women were soon spending time together every day, helping each other out. But after a few months, the Princes Hotel had become too expensive, and its few amenities had lost their charm for both women. It was becoming impossible and stressful for their small children to find somewhere indoors to play or even make a noise.

'I'd far rather be in a cottage than stuck here,' Audrie said one day. 'With a garden. Wouldn't you?'

They rented a house, Armitage, in nearby Glendale Crescent.

It would cost less than the hotel, allow them more space, and enable them to share the tasks of looking after the children. Audrie was able to write to Com to give him the good news, but her main priority had always been the baby.

Princes Hotel, Cape Town
Darling Mummy and Daddy
I think without doubt this is quite the foulest letter I've ever
had to write. It's Susan, poor lamb. For some time I've had
a suspicion that things were not quite right with her. She is now
ten months old and still looks about four months, so I thought
I'd take her to a specialist.
Last week they were both coughing so I saw the local GP.
After prescribing for them he asked me if the doctors in Ceylon
had ever told me what was wrong with Susan. I said they all,
including the specialists, had said she was very backward,
but just needed building up and would be all right in time.
The doctor thought it was more than that. I didn't know what
he was driving at, so asked him what he meant, and he told
me he thought she was a Mongolian.
Of course I had the most awful shock. He advised me to take her
to see Dr Rabkin, a well-known baby specialist. He wouldn't say
anything else, so as not to prejudice. I made a date to take her
to the specialist this morning. I knew what he was going to say as
he kept asking such leading questions. He was very nice and tried
to break the news gently but I knew what he was driving at so
asked him straight out, and he said she was definitely, but not a
bad case. He said these babies are recognisable when they're born!
What I feel is, why the HELL should my daughter be like that?
I can't think why they didn't tell me when she was born. I'm
sure Com didn't know or else I'm sure he would have told me
when I had recovered from having her. They occur quite often, the
specialist told me, but nobody knows the reason. It's nothing to

do with health or age or heredity or anything. It just happens.
She is such a lamb too, so happy, laughs and talks to herself all
the time. I don't think any lay person would know to look at her
in her cot, as you can see in the snaps.

I can't really make any plans till I hear from Com. I don't
suppose he'll know what to do either. The specialist says that
when she gets older, it won't be a good thing to bring them
up together.

I feel quite stymied. I haven't really realised it yet, although ever
since the Doctor told me I've noticed more things about her and
didn't have much hope. But you can't help having a little.

Don't worry about this too much darling Mummy. Joan, another
English evacuee who lives here at the Princes, often comes in the
evening with her son Richard and helps bathe Robin for me and
we have a chat together and a brandy and Ginger ale, which I've
taken to having now and again instead of whisky as it's much
cheaper out here.

I'm afraid this is a very depressing letter, but thought it would be
better to tell you as soon as I was certain myself. The specialist
and Joan both say I ought to put her into a Home, but I can't
bear the idea. I think I'll wait and see, until I find out what
Com thinks. It's all so terribly difficult.

Joan and I decided that since we'd been through this, we had
better stick together in future, so until we hear, we are going to
try and find a little place to share the rent. I've written to Com
and told him all this, or at least the parts which will get past
the censor.

With my love to you both,
Audrie

Laverstock, 27th August 1942

I have been making more enquiries about return permits, but I fear I'm not so optimistic as I was in my last letter. A planter who ran a big dairy, but whose military duties prevented him from looking after it, applied on those grounds for a permit to get his wife back from Africa and run it for him, but not a hope. However I will do my damnedest.

Rayner drinks all day, and Olive has gone quite peculiar again, since I hurt her feelings by refusing to go out with them, and as a reaction she's getting very bossy about the house. She decided that a blackout was too black and had moved the black paper from the lights. I promptly put it back again and had to tell her that the blackout responsibility is mine alone.

Laverstock, 31st August 1942

Got back here at 8.30 Sunday night from Kandy and would have clearly loved to have the bungalow to myself but as usual it was teeming with Rayners. I was irritated right away because I put 5 gallons in the tank on my way to the station on Thursday and when I got back there wasn't ½ gal left. Whenever I go away, he goes careering out to Mount Lavinia and all over the place and never thinks of petrol or wear and tear.

Another letter arrived today, you had just been to see the Home which is the one I presume you have fixed on for Susan. It must have been a bit of an ordeal especially seeing the other children. When I went to see Dr Da Silva he showed me a photo of a typical Mongol baby and it made me feel quite odd. However we've got to get used to that sort of thing. I can't tell you how glad I am that everything is fixed.

The Rayners have some other Singapore people coming in this evening and I'm going out. You will have gathered that I've been a spot irritated with the Rayners these last few weeks but don't worry. I quite enjoy it and I get so fed up without you, and it's nice to have someone to get cross with. Not that I'd ever need to get cross with you.

Laverstock, 3rd September 1942

My darling, today is the third anniversary of the war and reminds me of that grim day in Aberdeen. The clocks have been put back another half hour so it isn't dark till 7.30. It doesn't make much difference except that it's a hell of a long time to wait for the sun to go down.

Laverstock, Saturday 5th September 1942

Gerald Rayner locked himself in for two hours last night and wouldn't come out. Then they both went off late to the Garden Club and as usual having exhausted his drink ration there, Gerald went on to the Colombo club. He sent the driver back and didn't return until all hours.

George Stevenson returned last week. Amanda has got off with someone else in the meantime, making yet another matrimonial disturbance. It's a common saying in Colombo now that if you meet some friend you haven't seen for some time, it's safer not to ask how their husband or wife is.

The Rayners get so much on my nerves. He's constantly asking odd questions about the clubs and wanting to be introduced to people I don't know. What has really got my goat darling and you might as well know, is this: when I got your agonising news about Susan, I'm afraid that for the first time in my young life I had a bit of a breakdown. During the stress of it I had to tell someone and a few nights back I told Olive Rayner. One would surely think that that information received under such circumstances would be sacred. But I now know that Olive has blabbered all over the place. I have suspected this for some time and just to make certain I tackled them and found that half the club have been kindly informed by Olive.

It was not maliciousness which prompted it, but apparently a horrible conceit, the impression she tried to create was that she'd be the only one who knew, and was therefore my bosom pal to whom my confidences were confided. It makes me extremely sick and so now you know. I'm going to try and get rid of them.

Princes Hotel, Newlands, Cape Town,
5th September 1942
Darling Dads and Mums
Well, the deed is done. Susan went to the Home on Monday and touch wood is settling down quite well. The Dr has already seen her and seemed very pleased with the way she moved around, except for the fact that she is rather underweight. He put her on a fattening diet but says it really isn't surprising as she is teething.
She really is very active for her age and yelled her head off when I left her, but the Matron seemed really quite pleased as apparently they seldom mind who is with them. I felt very much happier about her yesterday, Matron told me she had eaten well, and was quite happy bouncing around her cot. This morning I took some things and everything seemed OK.
Robin misses her very much and keeps asking where she is. I sent you off the parcel while I was in Cape Town this morning, dried and tinned fruit and chocolate. Do let me know what you would like best and I'll send another parcel on later.

Laverstock, 9th September 1942
Just got your telegram saying that Susan is happily settled. Nice work and very comforting news, and a real triumph for you, my darling, after all your efforts. What an awful ordeal it must have been for you going to these institutions. This place sounds so much nicer and she'll probably get much more individual attention.
I'm as pleased as punch and all the minor irritations have disappeared like magic. I even like the Rayners much better now. In fact I like everybody better now. I'm going to give myself a half-holiday this afternoon just for fun. If I weren't doing my war stuff this evening I think I'd go on the tiles or something just to celebrate.
The said Rayners are off out again to god knows where this evening. Have no idea where their money comes from. They're

talking about taking a flat in Sellamatta Avenue. Personally
I don't mind whether it's in Timbuktu but it could be a great
relief to get rid of them.

c/o Colombo Apothecaries, 16th September 1942
I heard a lovely story up in Kandy last weekend. The District
Magistrates there, Collis and Endersby, took their Civil exams
at the same time, came out together, and are great pals. They
often meet up at the club, and last month they were cycling
home from dinner when they were stopped by a local policeman
for riding their bicycles without lights. He had no idea who
they were, they didn't tell him, and so they were both up on
a charge. This meant they'd have to appear in front of a local
magistrate – which of course would be one of them. So Collis
agreed he would sit when Endersby came up, and vice versa.
In court, two days later: Collis: 'Mr Endersby, you are charged
that on the night of 16th you were riding a bicycle without
front or rear lights after the official lighting up time, contrary to
the Road Traffic Act 1932, section 42. How do you plead?'
Endersby: 'Guilty, Sir.'
Collis: 'Very well. You are fined ten rupees.'
Endersby: 'Thank you, Sir.'
The next morning, Endersby was sitting when his friend came
up for trial.
Endersby: 'Mr Collis, you are charged that on the night of
16th you were riding a bicycle without front or rear lights after
the official lighting up time, contrary to the Road Traffic Act
1932, section 42. How do you plead?'
Collis: 'Guilty, Sir.'
Endersby: 'Very well. You are fined twenty-five rupees.'
Collis: 'Twenty-five? But yesterday I fined you only ten!'
Endersby: 'Maybe. But there has been far too much of this type
of behaviour recently and it's got to stop. Next Case.'

Thursday 17th September 1942

I went through all the old snaps and there were some of us when we were engaged and you were looking slim and beautiful. Not that you aren't looking slim now darling, and I am quite sure I will fall for you all over again, not that I have fallen out of love with you darling, but I'd better stop this as I seem to be tying myself up in knots.

I had to pitch into Olive last night, if only to stop her going on any more. It was really an unforgivable business her spouting out about Susan, and I don't see why she should be allowed to go on about our private affairs. She has certainly been in a frightful flat spin since, but however unpleasant it has been I think it was necessary. Laverstock will be a haven of peace if they go. I do hate all this unpleasantness even though I have to start some of it myself.

Laverstock, 6th October 1942

Back after a good weekend in Kandy with work at the Queen's, and generally feeling much the better for it. Had a foul journey down, pouring wet and one breakdown on the wiring system which took the driver an hour to put right. Spent another hour taking a child to hospital, which had been run down by a skidding car, said car having landed in the paddy fields 10 feet below the road.

About coming back here or going on home, my suggestion was entirely a selfish one as I am so mighty lonely without you. If you can get home and would feel better back with your parents I'll quite understand. Susan will have to be left alone but it all depends on how you feel. So long as you are reasonably happy there, it would be foolish to go on home to England, or come rushing back here. Anyway we can leave it until restrictions are relaxed.

What do you feel you'd like to do about Susan? After the war do you think it best to take her straight on home, or leave her in Cape Town and come back here? I so wish we could discuss it together.

Wednesday 9th October 1942

I gave Stuart a thrashing at chess last night and then we drifted across to the Colombo Club and had a couple of games of billiards. They only put two bottles in the bar at 7.00 PM and when that is finished you get no more. Needless to say there were many others in the club. The whisky situation is quite hopeless now the average private ration seems to be about one bottle per month. So I had to tell Gerald Rayner no more whisky drinking, there just aren't the stocks now. Funnily enough when I was writing the above, who should walk into the office but the appalling Olive. She asked me to go out to lunch with them next Sunday and I more or less had to tell her that apart from being in Kandy next Sunday I was booked up for the next three years.

14th October 1942

I sent off a cable today for your birthday and I hope very much that it's a nice one. I only wish I could spend it with you. Many happy returns and I'm picturing you guzzling down South African champagne if there is such a thing.

30th October 1942

My darling, many thanks for your cable which was waiting for me in the office this morning. 40 years old. Doesn't that sound awful. I feel like a Chelsea pensioner or something.

2nd November 1942

This is a great day. I opened the mailbag this morning and out poured your missing letters, seven of them in all. So, Robin did have whooping cough after all. Poor old you darling having to look after him night and day and not being able to see Susan at all. I expect if you woke up one morning and found there wasn't some new trouble looming up you'd wonder what had happened. The news about Susan is very encouraging and certainly confirms how right we were in putting her into the home. The Rayners are now quite notorious at the Garden Club, he for being invariably tipsy. I've been given some very sharp looks for having brought him there in the first place. She constantly makes a nuisance of herself in the bridge room. Several members refuse to cut in at any table she's playing at. It's rather like a Bateman cartoon, the look of furtive pain that comes on the faces of the other players when she puts in an appearance. As for him, now that he can't get any more whisky from the Apothecaries, I believe he is drinking some Australian stuff, which he mixes with Sherry. It seems to have the effect all right. **(Later)** *Rayner has just walked into my office, sozzled to bits as usual at 11.30 AM. His object in paying me a visit was to be put up as a full member of the golf club. As a Singapore refugee member he's allowed to play but not to use the bar,*

*so he's putting up his hundred rupees entrance fee to be a full
member. It's quite pathetic really. Don't know where he gets
the funds.*

*Just heard of the Americans landing in Africa. Everybody is
very optimistic. I said to Dan Langtree this morning, 'By Jove
it looks as if we're getting our wives back soon' and he said,
'My dear chap we'll be meeting them in London soon.' Maybe
it's not as bright as that but it does seem like the real second
front darling.*

---

20 November 1942 *Quite a day. At Pembroke on Sunday morning
Yoxall the intel officer came to see me in the decoding room. He asked if
I'd mind stepping into a private office. We left the hut and went along
to another at the end of the row, near Hopkins' office, a room I'd not
seen before. After a long couple of minutes of silence, two other men
crashed in, a red cap sergeant, and an army officer, must have been in
his fifties, who introduced himself as Colonel Ellis, Intelligence. Ellis
was a gigantic man, six foot five, with huge shoulders and a completely
shaven bald head. He sported the ribbon stripes of an MC.*

*He asked me to sit, but all three remained standing over me. I was
completely foozled and when I asked what was happening, nobody
answered. Ellis was holding a brown file, the same one that Hopkins
had when he interviewed me. 'What's your address?' Ellis asked. I gave
it. He ticked a paragraph on the open page in front of him.*

'How long have you been living there?'

'Since we were married in 1938,' I replied.

*'What else so you do in addition to your work here?' Ellis finally sat
down at the desk and stared at me with his pen poised.*

*'It's all on my file, there,' I protested. 'You have all that, you know it
all.' I had no idea what they were getting at.*

*'Tell us again,' Ellis snapped. I told them about the Apothecaries
business and the Kandy hotels.*

'And who else lives at Laverstock, Melbourne Avenue, with you?'

'My wife and children have been evacuated,' I said, 'so it's just me and the servants.'

'How many servants? Where are they from?' He pencilled further notes.

'All Sinhalese, all local. They've all been with us for years, since we were married.'

'Anyone else?'

'No. Well, yes, the evacuees, the Rayners. What's this about? My work?'

'Who? Who are the Rayners? No, not your work.'

I felt much better. 'Olive and Gerald. They're Singapore refugees, from the Duchess of Bedford, the ship,' I said. 'They were billeted on us by the Committee. Turned up with two suitcases and what they stood up in. We've given them clothes and taken them around. You must have a record of them.'

'That's a different department,' said Yoxall. 'We'll check them out. You can go back to your duties, thank you.' He closed the file, stood up and left the room. The sergeant escorted me back to our hut. There, I sat back down to work on the usual codes, but nobody else looked at me. It was all very quiet.

Three hours later, just as I was ready to go home after the shift, Ellis came back and asked me if I would mind coming with him again. His attitude had changed, more polite, slightly less on edge.

'What's happening,' I asked.

'You'll soon find out. Would you mind if we pay a visit to your house?'

'Of course not. But why?' I said. 'I haven't any whisky, Rayner's drunk it all.'

'You'll soon find out. This isn't a social call. Come on. Now. You can leave your car here.' Ellis jumped up and led the way out of the hut, with me, the sergeant and Yoxall following.

There were two cars waiting, an army MP car, with three red cap corporals, and a big Humber with a young officer waiting for us and an army corporal driver at the wheel. The lieutenant had the Royal Signals shoulder flash. Yoxall, Ellis, and I dived into the Humber. The MP Sergeant got into the second car and we started back into town, then turned south at Cinnamon Gardens towards Bambalapitya. The corporal drove very fast, with the MPs following. I asked again, *what's happening but they all kept mum. I just held on.*

We stopped at the top of the Avenue and the army car drew up next to us. Yoxall nodded across to the sergeant. One of the redcaps got out and stationed himself on the junction.

'How far down are you?' asked Yoxall. I was about to answer but was interrupted.

'About two hundred yards on the right?' the Signals lieutenant called out, looking at a street map. 'That's where we pinpointed the signal.'

'Yes, that's it.' I began to understand what was going on.

As we moved forward, Yoxall leaned out of the window and pointed at the house. The sergeant and one of the corporals jumped out, and the army car shot off to the far end of the Avenue. The Lieutenant rolled the Humber up to our front gate.

Ellis scanned the area. 'Laverstock? Is this it?' I nodded.

'Are they normally here at this time of day?'

'I've no idea. I'm usually at office.'

'OK, let's go, come on.' We got out of the car, I opened the gate and led the way up the drive to the porch. As usual, William appeared before I could put the key in the lock.

'Master?'

'William, it's all right, these men need to come in to the house. Is Mr Rayner at home?' The two MPs followed me and the three others into the hall. William looked at them in astonishment, especially at the pistols in their hands, their hairy knees and huge boots.

'Yes, Master, Lady has gone out but he is in their room.'

'Quick, which one is it?' said Ellis.

'Top of the stairs,' I said. 'First left. Brown door.'

The MPs slipped their safety catches. Ellis fiddled with his holster, pulling out his sidearm. 'Stay here, please,' he said.

They ran up the stairs, the MPs in front, and knocked on the door. I followed them up, but they didn't stop me. Nobody answered. I noticed several scratches on the door. Down in the hall, I could see William was joined by cook and the houseboy, staring up at us.

Ellis turned and whispered to me, 'Speak to him.'

'Gerald, it's Com,' I called. 'I need a word with you.'

There was a muffled reply and some shuffling. Twenty seconds later the door opened and a dishevelled Rayner appeared.

The two MPs grabbed him and pushed him back into the bedroom. By the time Ellis, Yoxall and I followed, my dressing room was like *A Night at The Opera*. Rayner, sitting on the bed, was wearing a vest and grey flannels, old ones I'd given him. For once he seemed sober, but he looked very tired and his hair, usually brushed straight back, was a mess.

'Where is it?' said Yoxall. 'And don't give me any "Where is what?", we know what you've been doing. We just want to know how and why.'

Rayner opened his mouth and gazed wildly around, but before he could speak, the two MPs started searching the room. In just a few seconds they found what they were looking for. They threw open my wardrobe door, and there on the bottom shelf was a small black transmitter. On his knees, the sergeant scrabbled around and found a cable running out of the window. He collected it up and sent the corporal downstairs with the apparatus.

We heard him shout and a few minutes later, the other two soldiers came upstairs, grabbed Rayner and hustled him out to the car. I never saw him again.

'We'll need to search the room more thoroughly later,' said Ellis. 'It'll need to be sealed.' He started writing in a small notebook.

'I'll tell William no one's to go in there,' I volunteered, as we turned to go back down the stairs. William was waiting, looking very bemused.

'Not enough,' Ellis rejoined. 'My chaps will seal it up officially until they can do the job properly.'

'Your chaps?' I said.

'Sorry. On a need to know basis. I'm sorry we had to put you through that. Would you like a ride back to your car?'

I accepted. As we drove back to Pembroke, not so fast this time, I asked them what would happen to Rayner.

'He'll be charged with espionage and possibly also treason,' said Yoxall. 'Death penalty.'

'Or we may use him for our own purposes,' said the Colonel. 'The MPs will come back and wait for Mrs R. D'you think she knows what her *husband was up to?'*

'Probably not.' I thought of Olive at the Garden Club bridge room, and how she had betrayed my confidences about Susan. 'She's a spot dim-witted, to say the least.'

Com's private life became calmer after the Rayners' departure. His war work and his regular office duties, both at the Apothecaries in Colombo and the hotels up in Kandy, with the four-hour train journey in between, meant that he was working sixty or seventy hours a week. However, he found time for his letters.

Laverstock, Melbourne Avenue

I just got three more letters from you darling and I'm feeling grand. We've finally got rid of the Rayners, but not in the way I expected. Can't tell you now but you will enjoy the story. A very exciting day.

You are having an awful time of it. Do whatever you like about finding a house to share with Joan, whether furnished or unfurnished and hang the expense for heaven's sake.

I was so happy to get your decision as to what you want to do when return here is possible. Let's hope that with the news continuing good it will soon be on. Sorry but there aren't any silk stockings at all here, but I will keep a lookout. In your last letter you rather burst out with how you want to get back darling. I got such a warm glow reading it because I am really getting quite desperate to see you and Robin again.

It is very nearly time to wish you a merry Christmas sweetheart. Will you please choose two whopping big presents for Robin's Christmas and on his birthday, with love from Daddy. I don't know what you did with the £15.00 on your birthday but I now insist that you spend at least £20.00 on an evening frock which you will wear at a certain little party of two at the Galle Face Hotel on Saturday night the ----th of ----- (please make it soon).

16th December 1942

Alasdair Nelson has been very ill in hospital after the Bengal cyclone. His battalion were in the thick of it and it was worse than any war. They lost many men drowned but did great work of rescue, after which they had to bury thousands of dead bodies, cattle etc. Alasdair had to swim for hours in floods littered with dead bodies, and that's where he picked up the bug which made him so ill.

29th December 1942

Gwyneth has apparently made £40.00 at bridge since she went to Durban. They are really an amazingly lucky couple. No wonder they called their daughter Bridget Bridget, after their principal source of income...

30th December 1942

Tomorrow is the last day of 1942 and a pretty foul year for the Sutherland family so let's hope 1943 will bring us better luck. My new year resolution is to do my damnedest to make up to you for all the troubles you have faced so courageously, so that when you get back I will be yours to command. I was before anyway, but you get what I mean.

2nd January 1943

New Year's Eve was pretty hectic all around and I've never seen the Galle Face so full. We had quite a good party but I feel I was rather forcing the party spirit as I was still missing you so dreadfully.

Almost every week, as the war news improved, Com recounted the rumours of the possibility of the expatriate wives soon being allowed to return. But his optimism was quashed when he attended a dinner for Colombo business executives with the Commander-in-Chief, Ceylon.

'I'd like to make it clear to you all,' said the C-in-C, 'there's no question of allowing expatriate wives to return, at least until the Japanese no longer dominate the Eastern Indian Ocean.' It was worse. No families would be allowed to return until Malaya was reoccupied, and that couldn't even be planned until Burma was clear of the Japanese.

Com wrote to the chief secretary to ask for Audrie's return on compassionate grounds. 'With the Mongoloid child and another small boy to look after,' he argued, 'it's not possible for her to care adequately for the family on her own.' But his request was politely turned down.

They both continued to worry about Susan's progress and wellbeing. But on her regular visits, Audrie could see that the little girl was finally thriving and happy in the Home, and these concerns diminished. 'The hardest part,' she wrote, 'is not being able to sit with you and discuss what to do for her.' They had to choose whether to bring her back to Colombo when the time came, to arrange a passage for her back to England, or even to leave her behind when Audrie could eventually return to Colombo.

After worrying about which of her family should have priority, Audrie decided that Robin and Com's health and happiness must come first. As long as Susan was well cared for, she wouldn't be aware of missing her mother or brother. Audrie would return to Ceylon with just Robin, as soon as it was permitted. With great relief at having made the decision, she wrote to tell Com and her parents.

Com's office and his study at Laverstock continue to fill a second role as Matrimonial Advice centres. For reasons he could never fathom, his Colombo acquaintances and friends continued to approach him seeking advice and guidance.

11th January 1943

I seem to be qualifying most unwillingly to be a divorce lawyer these days. I think I told you that young Joy Masters had gone haywire over a naval bloke and wanted to leave her husband. Well, when I got back from office yesterday she was waiting to see me, the said husband having returned and she didn't know where to go for advice. I told her not to be a bloody fool and to go back to her husband. Considering the other bloke also has a wife and kids my advice was reasonably sound. However, she was in a pretty massive flat spin, and would not listen much to reason.

This morning, who should walk into my office also seeking advice, but said husband. They are a very simple couple and don't really know anybody in Colombo except Joyce Blackwood, with whom she apparently quarrelled some time ago. It's not so much advice they want as sympathy. I must say it is a spot uncomfortable doing this father confessor stunt. She seems to think that you can just walk into a lawyers' office, pay sixpence, and get your divorce handed across the counter. It's quite a sad little mess up and heaven only knows where it will end.

Com suggested that as a non-essential European Resident, Joy Masters should follow the advice of the Commander-in-Chief and evacuate herself to South Africa. She duly surfaced in Cape Town, looked Audrie up, and spent the next week in the tiny kitchen at Glendale Crescent, pouring every sad detail of her love life into Audrie's sympathetic ear.

March 1943

Goodness, Mrs Sutherland, it's just on a whole year since you left now. Isn't it awful? I expect you've almost forgotten what I look like, so please just try and jog your memory a bit. You know, tall, curly-headed chap, with crooked nose?

In June 1943, *Eindhoven* returned to Colombo, this time laden with troops from the US, and that day, the intelligence officer Yoxall asked Com into his office for a quiet word.

He was much more charming than hitherto. He pushed back his chair, opened one of the side drawers in his desk, placed his feet on it, and slid a cigarette box across the desk, asking me to help myself.

Yoxall leaned forward to offer a light, and sat back blowing rings up towards the overhead fan, which promptly gusted them back in his face. Com wondered if the man had seen too many detective films.

'We've had some success,' Yoxall finally revealed. 'Rayner was using that machine to transmit details of shipping in Colombo harbour to the Japs. He brought it with him in pieces on the ship and re-assembled it in your room.' Com understood why he'd been so precious about the suitcases. 'His parents were Germans who moved to Japan before the first war. He grew up there.'

'But his English was perfect.' Com couldn't believe it.

'Went to the International School in Yokohama. His real name is Gerhard Rainer, with an I not a Y. Rainer had worked for Siemens in Japan and in those days the Kempeitai, the Jap secret service, had their eye on all foreigners.' His story was that the Kempeitai had blackmailed him, after he stole funds from his company, to pay for drink and God knows what else, Yoxall revealed. 'They gave him a fake British passport as Gerald Rayner, and sent him to Singapore to spy on the naval base. He married Olive there. When all the Europeans started preparing to leave he saw his opportunity and packed up to escape with the others.'

'Why didn't anyone spot him?' Com asked. 'Surely in Singapore the Europeans all knew each other, same clubs and so on?'

'He kept himself to himself,' Yoxall said. 'His wife had no idea what was going on. We checked with a couple of dozen other Singapore refugees and none of them had ever heard of Gerald Rayner. And he wasn't even registered on the *Duchess of Bedford.*'

As the months wore on, all European men in Colombo had one thing in common – the absence of regular mail deliveries. Like small children at boarding school, urgently expecting a postal order, the group of stranded husbands spoke of very little except the next mail.

'Brokers, soldiers, tinkers, tailors, and social prejudice,' Com wrote, 'break down under the common sorrow.'

When you meet a chap now you don't say 'Fine morning',
you say, 'Any post?' In club bars there is no other topic of
conversation. Anybody who has had a letter doesn't mention
it. He would be torn in little pieces bit by bit.

A Durban husband blames the censor, and gets into a heated
argument with a Grahamstown husband who's convinced that
it's lack of aeroplanes. A Johannesburg husband says it's the
monsoon, and is immediately called a fathead by
a Pietermaritzburg husband. And so it goes on until the bar
closes, which is very early these days. Cape Town husbands
being very much in the minority are contemptuously ignored.
But if some bright spark suggested that it's because they've got
to wait for the mails from Cape Town, then he would have to
seek police protection immediately.

Monday 5th July 1943
I got a letter from brother Tom, giving me some news of a big
raid on Aberdeen, about 800 houses destroyed or damaged by
about 120 big bombs. Casualties were heavy he says, but can't
give details. Tom says he had the door handle of his car shot off
by a machine gun from a Dornier III 150 feet above him, but
it doesn't seem to have worried him much. He was busy all the
time ferrying casualties to the First Aid Post.

Wednesday 7th July 1943
Poor old Wilf got his spare car tyre pinched the other night.
Tyres are absolutely unobtainable and so he is in a bit of a panic.
My own spare is now under lock and key in the bungalow.

Finally, the summer brought the news all the solitary husbands had been waiting for.

Colombo, 25th August 1943

My darling heart, isn't it absolutely marvellous news? Right out of the blue I just picked up my Times, and there was the headline 'Wives Allowed To Return'. When I rang up Wilf, the blighter had already got his cable off to Gwyneth. However I sent you one right away and I am waiting for your reply. In the meantime I've written to the Chief Secretary applying for the required permit. I don't suppose for one minute that you'll be able to catch a ship right away because passages must be pretty scarce and there are about 2000 women waiting to get back. I hope there that you've seen Thomas Cook or somebody and found out the form. It's important that you find either a fast ship or one in convoy but I can at least expect to see you back in time for Christmas now. Oh boy, it's almost unbelievable. I feel like a prisoner condemned to penal servitude who suddenly gets handed a reprieve.

The only stipulation made by the C-in-C is that returning wives will not require hotel accommodation or otherwise interfere with general accommodation in Colombo, but there again we needn't worry. The other topic of conversation now is whether there are any ships available.

I remember when you went off and we tried to look upon it as a few months' holiday. Nearly 18 months now and it's such a relief to know that anyway it's not going to be another 18 months. The general feeling is that the actual passage will be pretty safe. I've arranged for the Ceylon Government to cable your permit directly to the powers that be in Cape Town and all you have to do is to go to the passport office in Cape Town and enquire about it. It will no doubt be there already registered.

But Com didn't mention to his wife that the newspaper item also carried a warning from Government House:

The risks of enemy attacks on Ceylon, or on ships on passage to Ceylon, still exist and those who elect to invite women and children to cross the sea in present circumstances must consider the dangers involved.

Steuart Place, Colombo, 30th August 1943

My darling heart, thank you so very much for the lovely cable, it sent my heart up into the clouds and I've been rushing around with a perpetual grin on my face ever since. I've just had confirmation that your permit has been cabled off. I sent off another cable this morning giving full particulars. I have no idea of course when you will be able to get a ship but as quite a few husbands had cabled their wives on the same point, I'm optimistic that maybe there will be one soon.

You asked what things are impossible to obtain here, and it would be wonderful if you can bring some with you if obtainable in Africa. Lipstick, rouge, face cream, stringent, face powder, are all very rare. And if you can get hold of any golf balls for me at any price please do so. About golf balls, my conscience is clear.

For Audrie and the other South Africa evacuee families, the news meant another long wait. 'Be ready and packed,' said the travel authorities. 'You will be contacted at short notice as soon as a berth is available.' But they didn't say if it would be a week or a month.

Audrie went to see the Hospital, and told them the news. 'Not to worry,' said the kind matron. 'We'll make sure she's well looked after, and then when all this is over, you can decide what you want to do.' Perhaps Audrie and Com would come back and take Susan with them when they returned to England after the war.

She packed and unpacked her luggage several times, but in the event it was December before the news came through. *You will please report with this letter to the Port Authority offices on 17th of December*, said the letter allocating her and Robin a berth on the *Duchess of Cambridge* which would sail that evening for Colombo. Her happiness at finally being able to set out for Ceylon was muted by the knowledge that she wouldn't see Susan again, at least not until the end of the war.

As the tugs nudged the *Duchess of Cambridge* slowly into Colombo harbour, Audrie stood at the rail, with Robin at her side, searching across at the throng at the landing stage for any sign of her husband.

Landfall and departure mark the rhythmical swing of a seaman's life and a ship's career, Aunt Peggy had said. The phrase wouldn't stay out of her mind. Since then, she'd taken six long sea passages and each one had brought a new chapter to her life. She'd been torpedoed, they'd been separated, she'd had to leave her baby in a Home, and now, a new chapter. They'd be back together again. But would it be like before? She was no longer the naïve young girl who'd been terrified of running a bungalow. Would he still feel the same about her, after nearly two years apart?

She stared down at the crowd, but he wasn't there. Probably stuck in the office or on war work, she guessed. She would have to carry on and get home, surprise him later. But yes, there he was, holding his hat and peering up at the ship. Her darling husband.

Audrie leaned forward over the rail, stuck two fingers in her mouth, and gave an ear-splitting whistle. Com turned immediately, spotted her and waved his hat. She waved furiously back at him, feeling her eyes starting to mist, then picked Robin up and ran with him down to the embarkation deck, weeping with happiness.

A little more than a year later, on VE Day, 8 May 1945, Com and Audrie joined Sir James and Lady Berry and several other friends, for a special dinner at Justice House, before driving out to see the celebrations. The Governor's Residence was floodlit in pale rose and turquoise, with the letters GR and the imperial crown, all lit by strings of bright bulbs, while the Galle Face Hotel and many public buildings in Fort had joined in the celebrations with huge illuminated V-signs.

When they came by the clock tower again at nearly midnight,

Audrie wrote, there were scores of people still about. 'We could hardly get through the crowd, and a crowd of sailors, cheerful but rather worse for wear, tried to jump onto the car.'

But until at last Japan could finally be beaten, Com's war work would have to continue. And finally, after so many messages, about so many ships lost to Japanese submarines, came the sweet revenge he and his FECB colleagues had been longing for.

I was on duty for the 4 pm to 8 pm watch, when Baker the senior translator came over with a newly intercepted but incomplete message, sent using the newest code.

The Japs were anxious to get a supply convoy, guarded by a cruiser and a submarine, from Singapore to their airbase in the Andaman Islands. This new message carried the Japanese Naval HQ call sign, and they suspected it might lay out the plans. Com started work on it at about four thirty, and as they made progress, Baker alternately phoned intelligence with more scraps of the message and then suggested words which they could try to insert in the unsolved columns. By nine pm they could see that the messages revealed the map coordinates of the meeting point for the Japanese convoy and the route it would take. Once Com's colleagues had passed the details up to operations, he went home and slept for 12 hours, 'feeling that for once,' as he wrote, 'I'd made a real contribution.'

The result of their work was the last naval engagement of the East Indies Fleet, on 15 May 1945. Five destroyers, HMS *Saumarez*, *Virago*, *Vigilant*, *Verulam* and *Venus*, had set out from Trincomalee to confront the Japanese convoy, which included one of the biggest Japanese warships still afloat, the heavy cruiser *Haguro*, 13,000 tons and capable of 33 knots. The Royal Navy had caught up with them in the area between Sumatra and the Malay Peninsula, and after a night battle, had sunk *Haguro* in the Strait of Malacca.

'How did it go?' Com asked as he returned from the Apothecaries the next day. 'What did the doc say?'

'Darling, Van Langenberg says it's perfectly all right. There's absolutely no risk of having a second mongoloid baby.' Audrie looked at him with a confident smile, but she still wasn't one hundred percent certain.

'What does he know? He had no idea what was wrong with little Susan.'

'Yes, you're right. I certainly gave him a piece of my mind about all that. But after you told him and showed him my furious letter, he was so alarmed at not having known, not having diagnosed her at the beginning, that he's been looking it all up, the latest medical research. They say there's only a risk if the mother is much older. I'm not even thirty yet, he says it's nothing to worry about. And I'm due in mid-October.'

Resting at home as much as possible, Audrie hardly noticed as Ceylon became crowded with more and more servicemen, preparing for Operation Zipper, to drive the Japanese out of Malaya, until they read in *The Times of Ceylon* that atomic bombs had been dropped on Hiroshima and Nagasaki, which finally put an end to the Japan war.

In October, to Com and Audrie's great joy, she gave birth in the Joseph Fraser Nursing Home to a healthy baby son. The only drawback, as she wrote, was the same brain-fever bird still making its eerie call outside her window all night. 'He already has a few copper-coloured hairs,' she wrote to her mother, 'and Com is so pleased that we decided to call him Alasdair, he says it means red-haired king in the original Gaelic.'

Once the new baby was safely back at Laverstock, Audrie and Com could confirm their plans to start a new life back in Britain.

Grace Cottage, Piltdown, Sussex,
17th November 1945

Dear Com

Thanks for your letters and we are so pleased to hear that you and Audrie and the boys are coming home for good next year. Congratulations on the new job you have landed, it really sounds splendid. Thinking of Robin's schooling, why don't you send him to a Scottish school, they turn out the best men!

As ever

Finch

But as I knew, they never did come home together. When When I was just eight months old, my father was killed. Audrie, just thirty, was a widow with three children under eight.

THREE

1990s

Even though the letters and papers had given me a clear picture of their life together, those same questions were still unanswered. What happened to Susan? Why did Audrie never talk about her, or Com, or any of it?

I could understand how my parents had coped with the outcome of their decision to leave the little girl in a home – and from the letters, I now knew where it was, the Alexandra Hospital in Western Cape. There was nothing to suggest that Com and Audrie had ever seen her again. By today's standards, to have put her there seemed like a cruel decision. But how hard it had been for my mother, especially later on when she looked back. Surely it would have made it easier to bear if Audrie had talked about her with me and Robin.

Other letters showed that she'd kept in touch with the Alexandra nursing staff, and although the care was free, had posted cash every year to the Friends of the Alexandra, for them to buy Susan's birthday and Christmas presents. She must have seen how over the intervening fifty years, extraordinary changes had taken place in attitudes to the condition. The cruel name of 'Mongolian' had been officially changed to 'Down's syndrome' in the Sixties, and with new understanding, sufferers could now grow up as loved members of their own family.

Perhaps we'd be able to fly down to Cape Town one day to go and see her? I found a number online, called the Alexandra Hospital, and spent ten minutes identifying myself to an admin officer. 'No, I'm sorry,' I told the bureaucrat. 'I can't put Mrs Audrie Sutherland on the line, she's unfortunately no longer with us. If she were still alive, it would be her calling you, not her son.'

Once I was through to a manager, it was only to be told that I was too late. 'I do remember Susan, Mr Sutherland,' the woman said, 'but I'm sorry to tell you that she died, it was about ten years ago, can't be sure.'

Ten years ago? Susan would have been about fifty. There was nothing in the archive about her death.

'I'll send you an application form,' she continued, 'to fill in and send back, so that we can access the records and send them out to you. We'll need to see your sister's birth certificate and your mother's death certificate, for data protection purposes.'

When I put down the telephone, I felt ineffably sad. My elder sister had died, before I'd even known she existed. I remembered that extraordinary letter written after the ship was torpedoed, when Audrie'd said Com knew she was safe and out of danger, before he even knew she wasn't. This felt the same.

'Three of your family have died since you brought those letters home,' Felicity said. 'Haven't you gone far enough?'

She was right. 'But I still don't know what happened that night.'

'Snakebite? It was a shock, a terrible tragedy,' Felicity reminded me. 'She must have been totally devastated.'

'Maybe more to it than that,' I said. 'Why wouldn't she talk about it, even sixty years later? What did she mean, that time she said she was always thinking about what she could have done?'

'We'll never know, now. No more leads to follow. You might as well resign yourself.' She picked up a newspaper and began to read.

That seemed to be that. My project had come to a halt, or more likely, to its end. I'd been through the entire bundle, the letters, the aerogrammes, the notebook, the whole archive. On top of that, I'd visited the Colindale Newspaper Library, researched the old shipping line passenger lists, and spent days in the Imperial War Museum document rooms. I now knew a great deal more about my father and mother, and their life together. But that one detail still eluded me.

By now, it was too late. Most of that generation were gone. My mother had taken her secret, if there was a secret, to her grave. My brother was dead, and I knew that my sister, also gone, would never have known either. So it didn't look as though there was going to be a satisfactory end to the story.

Felicity and I sat in the warm kitchen in London, opening the usual depressing post-Christmas bills and credit card statements.

'This one's a card, been forwarded twice, it's addressed to your mother, at home and then forwarded to Manorfield,' said Felicity. 'Must have been sent on by their admin office.' She slid a large white envelope across the table. Inside was a Christmas card with the celebrated skating minister. A message on the left-hand side was written in a beautiful, old-fashioned italic hand.

> *Dearest Audrie,*
> *How are you? Well, and thriving, I hope. What news of*
> *Robin and Alasdair and their families? All is fine here, touch*
> *wood, only a few more aches and pains. It seems an age since*
> *we've got together for a natter, and I'm now so decrepit that*
> *I sometimes fear we shall never manage to see each other again.*
> *Perhaps I could persuade one of my brood to drive me over to*
> *you? Michael is living very near here now and is semi-retired –*
> *which makes me feel even older. Do let's speak in January.*
> *With love for Christmas and a Happy New Year.*
> *G*

'Gee?' Felicity looked up from her pile of waiting letters.

'It's G for Gertie, Gertie Larsen,' I said. 'My godmother. She was a friend of my Ma and Pa in Ceylon.'

'How come she hasn't heard Audrie died? Or Robin?' Felicity wondered. 'You'd expect the word to have spread around all the old Ceylon types by now?'

'I didn't think of her when Audrie died,' I admitted. 'She probably doesn't get out much. As she says herself, she's getting on. There's no address given. I'll see where she lives.' I rose and crossed the hall into the study, to fetch my mother's old address book, and returned, thumbing through the pages to L.

'Here we are, Larsen, Gertie, there are three old addresses crossed out. She's living in a care home, North Berwick, near Edinburgh, probably doesn't see many people.'

'Or read the death notices,' Felicity observed.

'Don't know why I didn't think of her at the time,' I said. 'But I haven't seen her, oh, since I was about ten. She drove across Europe with Audrie to Athens in nineteen fifty-four. I should call her with the sad news, hope it doesn't upset her.'

'This'd be a good time, right now,' Felicity pointed out. 'Six thirty. Drinks time.'

I went to the telephone in the study and dialled the number. It was picked up immediately and loudly. 'Yes?'

'Gertie Larsen? Gee?'

'Yes. Who is this?'

'It's Alasdair Sutherland, Auntie Gee. Audrie's son. Is it a good time to talk?' I hadn't called anyone Auntie since I was fifteen.

'Good Lord. Alasdair, darling boy, how are you, yes, but you'll have to speak up, I'm deaf as a post, let me just turn this thing up.' There was a buzzing on the line. 'That's better.' Her voice became even louder. 'How're your mother and Robin? Where are you speaking from? Aberdeen?'

'Gertie, I'm sorry to bring bad news. We're at home in London. Your Christmas card to Audrie has been sent on to me by the home where she lived. I'm afraid she died back in October. And Robin, two years before. I'm so sorry we didn't manage to let you know.'

There was a long silence, as I wondered how the old girl would take the news. Felicity walked into the study and handed me a glass of wine.

'I was there, you know,' Gertie boomed.

'You were where?' I indicated to Felicity to move nearer. She sat on the corner of my desk.

'I was there, with them, that night. In Colombo. When he was killed. I was staying with them at Laverstock. I'd come down from Pedro.'

I didn't know who or what she meant by Pedro. Startled, I turned to Felicity. 'Did you hear that? Gee was there when my Pa was killed.'

She nodded her head. 'But where?'

I put the phone back to my ear. 'Gertie, I'm astonished. I know nothing about this. Audrie never spoke about that day.' I pulled out a chair from beside the desk and sat down.

'She didn't? Oh, I'll tell you,' Gertie exclaimed. 'I'll tell you all about that evening. I knew Com long before, he was my first boyfriend when I came out in thirty-four.' She sighed and her voice dropped. 'Oh, I'm so sorry Audrie's gone. We've been friends for sixty years.' There was a pause and then her tone became more level. 'You'd better come and see me up here, and we can have a good natter.'

'Gertie, how kind, yes I'd love to. Is this your address I've found in Audrie's book, Haddington House?'

'Yes, that's it. But come soon,' she laughed, 'I'm already ninety-three. Next week if you like, I've nothing else to look forward to, what about Wednesday? I'll have a think about those days and tell you.'

'Excellent. Wednesday then, that'll be March 15. Felicity and I will come together and we can take you out for lunch. Until then, goodbye.'

I put down the phone, picked up my glass again, and we sat in thought for a while.

'This is becoming very Agatha Christie. She was there when he was killed, and she'll tell us all about it. D'you fancy a trip up to Edinburgh next week? And who or where was Pedro?'

The following Tuesday, I telephoned Gertie Larsen again, to confirm the lunch date. I booked a table at Ducks in Aberlady, a few minutes from Haddington, on the coast. By now very experienced at taking elderly deaf ladies out to lunch, I asked for a table against the wall, in the quietest part of the restaurant.

The next morning we took the shuttle to Edinburgh, and soon after midday we were in a rented car on the A1 towards Haddington. The care home was in Paterson Place, and once inside a large reception area, where several elderly residents were reading newspapers, we approached the glass window of an office.

'We've come for Mrs Larsen,' I announced. 'We're the Sutherlands. We're taking her out for lunch. She said she'd be in the lounge; can we go through?'

'Of course, please follow me.' The manageress led the way to a sitting room, and as soon as I saw her pushing herself out of a corner armchair, I recognised my godmother, although it had been more than forty years since we'd last met. Still tall and lean, Gertie wore a smart blue wool trouser suit and appeared at least ten years younger than her declared ninety-three. She leaned her stick against the back of a chair, held both hands out in greeting, and kissed us both

'Dear Alasdair, how lovely to meet Felicity, and for you both to come all the way to see an old lady.'

As Felicity drove to the restaurant, Gertie chattered on about the last time she'd seen Audrie, and what had happened to her children and grandchildren. Once at the table, after the waiter had poured three glasses of wine, Gertie paused, glancing between us as though she had prepared a speech.

'As you know, Audrie and I always kept in touch,' she started. 'And again, I'm so sorry to learn that she's gone, I will miss her so much.' She raised her glass. 'Here's to her memory.'

'To Audrie.'

'And now,' she smiled at us both. 'Since you called, I've been thinking back. How awful it must have been for her that day. You said, she'd never told you about that evening, but I was there, as I said.' She took another quick sip.

'Gertie, thank you so much,' Felicity interjected. 'It's very important for us. Alasdair's been wondering about this since Audrie died. She never spoke about Com or their life in Ceylon.'

'Very well, this is what happened.' She put her fingers on the table and took a slow breath. 'Com, Audrie and I were at Princes Club, where he had been playing in the finals of their snooker tournament. When we left, as we were getting into the car, Com trod on a snake, which bit him on the ankle. I had seen this happen before to one of our staff on the estate, and as he fell to the ground, more in shock I suppose, I remembered what to do and cried out to Audrie, "Bite it. Quick. Suck out the poison."'

Felicity's eyebrows went up. 'D'you mean – you'd seen this happen before?'

Gertie nodded. 'Snakes are common up-country. I suppose, now, that it must have been a Tic Polonga.'

Felicity's eyes widened. 'What's a Polonga? Is it a viper?'

'A sort, yes, Russell's Viper,' Gertie said. 'One or two of our people, pickers or estate workers, out in the gardens, would be bitten every year, normally it would make them ill for a day or so but very rarely serious or fatal. That's what made this so awful. Audrie was horror-struck. Poor lamb, she'd screamed at first when she saw the snake but then froze, she couldn't bring herself to get down and bite it. She stared at Com's leg. "I can't," she said, "I just can't."'

So that's what Audrie had meant when she'd said she'd 'never stopped thinking about it'. Felicity was watching me as we listened, and as I caught her glance, she closed her eyes in horror.

'The night watchman rushed forward,' Gertie went on, 'and massaged Com's leg downwards until a little blood came, then he said it was all right, and we got into the car and rushed to the doctor. We were there within seven minutes of Com having been bitten. The doctor cut it open and cauterised it, but Audrie then insisted on taking him to Dr Spittel's clinic.

'Com was marvellous and laughing and joking with us all in his usual style, and refused to stay overnight in the Spittel Home. He got up and walked down and got into the car. We thought it couldn't have been very poisonous as he was so bright and cheerful and with a lot of these bad snakes the effect is very quick. We went home to Melbourne Avenue. But soon afterwards, he got a headache and had a very restless night, until about four am when he started vomiting and his eyes were affected. She called the doctor again, and we took him back to the clinic at about five am. Even then we didn't realise how bad he was.'

Gertie paused and sat back in her chair as the waiter arrived with the starters. 'Do go on,' I said once he'd gone, 'what happened? How long did he survive?'

Gertie picked up a fork and turned it over in her hand. 'Only a few hours, I'm afraid. Audrie was with him all the time, but kept saying to me, "I couldn't do it, just couldn't do it." Anyway, most of the next day he had awful haemorrhages. I went back to Laverstock to be with the children for a while. The medics assured Audrie that if he could fight it, and keep his strength up for twenty-four hours, he would be all right. She was with him all the time, but he died at about five. It was impossible to grasp that he'd been full of life and joy one day and gone the next.'

Gertie resumed eating, and there was a silence as we took in what we'd learned. Then, Gertie reached across, took my hand and I noticed the sparkle of the old Ceylon diamond ring against her freckly brown skin.

'Darling Alasdair, your Mama was simply wonderful and so brave. She never even cried. He was buried next day. I went to the funeral with her and Gwyneth. The flowers were lovely and all Com's friends from everywhere were there.'

'We went to see his grave, eighteen months ago,' said Felicity, 'when we went for a tour. Alasdair had it cleaned up.'

Gertie paused. 'The thought of her there, all alone with you two, and poor Susan in South Africa, just makes me start even now.' Felicity opened her bag and handed Gertie a hanky. 'Do go on.' Gertie touched the corners of her eyes with the handkerchief, handed it back, and I noticed that my wife's eyes were shining too.

'Gertie, you are wonderful, remembering all this,' I said. 'But now, do take a rest.' We ate in silence for a while, and after dabbing her mouth with the huge linen napkin, Gertie continued.

'Afterwards, just to give you the whole story, Audrie wanted to keep to their original plan, to pack up for home and leave in July. I offered to help manage the packing if she wanted to get away sooner. But she wanted to have something definite to work on.' The waiter came to remove our plates.

'Then, when the time came, Ham and Peggy Mann, the Amhursts and I came to the port to see you off.' Gertie leaned back in her chair, still visibly moved by the memories. 'Waiting about at the port before she took you on board, we were all so upset, but Audrie was extraordinarily calm, wanting only to talk about the future.'

She stopped abruptly, and seemed deflated, as though the remembering had taken something out of her. Felicity gently moved the conversation on.

'Gertie, what about you and your family? How long did you stay in Ceylon?'

'We finally came home in fifty-one, after Independence, when the boys were ready to start school.' Gertie recalled, now smiling at us both, pleased at the change of subject. 'Larsen took a post with the British Council, in Athens. Audrie and I drove his car out there.'

That seemed to be all Gertie wanted to say about those days. Afterwards, returning to Haddington House, we helped her out of the car as the manageress came out to greet her.

'Thank you so much for your memories,' I said, hugging my godmother. 'And I'm so pleased we finally know what really happened.'

'Should have come up years ago,' Gertie retorted. 'I'm so glad to have at least seen you again, even if your dear Mama has gone now. Thank you for the lunch. Keep in touch.'

'What did you think of that?' Felicity asked as we drove on to Edinburgh Airport. 'Was that what you expected, about biting it?'

'I'm astonished. She remembered everything. She must have held the memory of that evening as vividly as Audrie did. I suppose I had some idea that something had happened that night, that Ma always felt responsible for. But it turns out that it was the opposite, it was what didn't happen.'

On the flight back to Heathrow, we were seated apart, and then the Piccadilly Line was crammed with Swedish visitors, so it wasn't until we were home, later that evening, that we could talk about Gertie's story.

'Do you think that's why Audrie never spoke about it?' Felicity wondered. 'Because she felt guilty that she could have saved him? If only she'd been strong enough to suck out the poison?'

'What else would it have been? She may not have been strong enough to cope then, but maybe that's what made her so capable later.' This was the only possible solution. If there was a different reason why Audrie had never spoken about Com's death, I would never find it now.

'Remember what Gertie said,' Felicity pointed out. '"Audrie never even cried at the funeral, just a day after he died."'

'I wonder if it's true,' I said. 'Does it work? Sucking out the poison, I mean.'

'It may be a myth, just Hollywood stuff. Why don't you look it up?'

I opened the laptop and a few minutes later, found the answer. 'Listen to this,' I read, 'from Web MD.'

...there are a number of productive things you can do to help a snakebite victim; but trying to suck out the venom isn't one of them. It's an act in futility that simply delays proper treatment. Indeed it has a negative effect, potentially further damaging the tissue around the bite and thus helping to spread the venom. Once it's in the body, snake venom quickly spreads throughout the victim's lymphatic system, and it is just not possible for a human to suck fast or hard enough to remove enough of it to have any real positive effect.

'She must have lain awake for nights, months, even years,' Felicity wondered, 'thinking about that moment and whether she might have saved him. And it was all completely wasted, it never could have worked. Couldn't she have ever asked someone?'

'Probably not,' I agreed. 'She would have had to admit that she hadn't been able to do it.'

Audrie was brought up to be the type of Englishwoman who could always cope, but, this one time, she hadn't. She'd felt guilty about not saving him, or not doing what she might have done, so avoided ever talking about that evening. As a result, she had tried to train Robin and me to be the same – independent, capable.

Felicity interrupted my thoughts. 'Darling, is that why she sent you out to catch the bus on your own at the age of four? Why you were sent away to school at seven? Why you spent summer holidays at a camp? Why she never pushed you or attempted to guide your life? To learn to cope? To be tough? To compensate for having no father?' She paused, but went on grinning.

'D'you think she planned it?' My mind was whirring as I tried to refocus my life from this new perspective.

'I'll tell you what she did,' Felicity laughed, stabbing her finger at me. 'Like it or not, she turned you into the most self-reliant person I've ever known. With you, it's not just the usual business of men never asking directions. You never ask for any help. You've no idea what it means to lack confidence. You depend on nobody.'

It began to make sense. 'Yes,' I acknowledged. 'She never wanted to talk about any problem, or ask for help, and so I thought that's what you do. You're right, she gave us the confidence to try anything. I was thrilled to be the only one who caught the school bus on his own. Summer camp at nine? It was much more fun than being at home on my own, with nobody else to play with. And she knew I loved Tizer.'

Felicity stood up, moved behind my chair, put her arms round my neck, and with her face next to mine, whispered, 'I know, I know. That's why you married me. Someone who does want to talk. About everything. I'll start dinner.'

ACKNOWLEDGEMENTS

I am especially grateful to friends and members of my family who have generously given their time and advice in the preparation of this book, especially, Geoffrey Aquilina Ross, Michael de St. Croix, Josephine Grever, Virginia Ironside, Mary Killen, Willie Landels, Nirmala de Mel, Sally Riley Gilbey, Tessa Greene Robbins, Harry Williams and Simon Williams.

Virginia, Mary, and Simon, all successful writers, patiently endured many discussions over the long gestation of this story, and read the final draft. I am particularly indebted to each of them for their suggestions and guidance.

My thanks also go to the following individuals and institutions for their recollections, advice and assistance: Joe Clark, Richard Doudney of the Ceylon Association, Brigadier David Innes, Lorna Howard Townsend, in Australia, former *Orontes* passenger Rosalie Lucas, Members of the Ceylon Golf Society, Staff at the Station X Museum, Bletchley Park, Staff at the Imperial War Museum, Department of Documents, and Staff at the British Library Newspaper Archive, Colindale (now at Boston Spa, West Yorkshire, and the British Library, St Pancras).

Thank you all, for the time you gave and the trouble you took, over the trouble I gave and the time I took.